DEEP ANALYSIS

By the same Author

BOOKS:

Clinical Psychology
(*George Allen & Unwin Ltd.*)

War in the Mind
Second Edition.   Macaulay Press

SCIENTIFIC PAPERS:

The Unconscious Significance of Hair

Clinical Notes on Epilepsy

Clinical Notes on the Analysis of a War Neurosis

Some Implications of Short Treatment

Mysterious Illness

The Psychology of Punishment

etc., etc.

(*Internat. Jl. Psycho-Anal.*
Brit. Jl. Med. Psychol.
The Yearbook of Psychoanalysis)

DEEP ANALYSIS

The Clinical Study
of an
Individual Case

by

CHARLES BERG

M.D.(LOND.), D.P.M.

Fellow of the British Psychological Society

*Physician to the British Hospital for Functional Mental
and Nervous Disorders*

*Physician to The Institute for the Scientific Treatment
of Delinquency*

late Hon. Physician to the Tavistock Clinic, London

London
GEORGE ALLEN & UNWIN LTD

FIRST PUBLISHED IN 1947
SECOND EDITION 1950

PRINTED IN GREAT BRITAIN
BY BRADFORD & DICKENS
LONDON, W.C.1.

CONTENTS

BOOK ONE

FATHER

BOOK TWO

MOTHER

BOOK THREE
SON

BOOK ONE
FATHER

Chapter I

The First Interview

YEARS AGO I was consulted by a young man who exhibited none of the usual symptoms presented by the majority of nervous patients. Moreover, he was exceptionally well endowed physically, mentally and scholastically.

At first it was impossible to classify him under one of the standard labels such as that of Anxiety State, Hysteria, Obsessions, Phobias, Hypochondria, Impotence, Depression, or even as a Characterological disorder. But as investigation proceeded it became increasingly clear that this case, perhaps by virtue of his freedom from overt symptoms, shed an unusually penetrating light upon the psychopathology of all nervous and mental illnesses; and, what was even more absorbingly interesting, upon the fundamental structure of normality itself.

It was on this account that I was tempted to record his analysis stage by stage in the hope that I would be able to convey to others interested in the subject the insight gained from a study of this clinical material.

The presence of nervous or mental illness may, or may not, be revealed by certain manifestations or symptoms, and though to the uninitiated these seem to be the essentials of the illness, a little deeper study shows us that this is not the case. Whatever symptoms may be manifested, further investigation invariably shows that they are but the latest method of outlet of the dynamic energy of primary urges (together with opposing or inhibiting elements) which have been denied expression in their original form.

The symptoms which this patient presented at his first interview were so vague and puzzling that the inexperienced observer might be excused from wondering whether he had indeed any symptoms at all, whether there was any need for him to consult a psychologist.

I asked him: "What makes you consult me? What makes you think that you require analytical treatment?"

He thought for a moment, and then said:

"Well, I suppose it is because I am very anxious to make the best use of what mental qualities I have got, and in my present state I do not think I am able to do this. I have given the matter a lot of thought, and it occurred to me that if one has toothache one goes to a dentist."

This last remark was infinitely more significant than the patient even dimly suspected, but of course it would have been inappropriate to hint at an interpretation at this point.

In the case of this patient it was only after a considerable period of analysis that one could reach any degree of clarity about his complaint. Therefore we may excuse him for being so vague and puzzled about it at the first interview. It seemed that all he was aware of was that things were not right, life was not satisfactory.

He naturally brought his intelligence to bear upon his problem, and therefore invented a series of rationalizations to account for what may have been nothing more than a sense of something wrong. These rationalizations he presented to me at the interview, though I noted at the time that he had often to think rather hard to find out what they were. He seemed to have increasing difficulty in justifying his conviction that he ought to be analysed. For instance, after a few moments of deep thought he would say:

"Yes, there is another point: I am always losing interest in one thing and picking up another. I hesitate too long. I am always dithering and procrastinating. I have now hesitated four times in writing a letter which is overdue. It seems I am for ever putting the jelly into shape instead of eating it.

"I have tried to analyse this myself, and I have come to the conclusion that it is due to mental inefficiency. I have a similar hesitancy in social matters.

"All my life I have been fed with stories of what a fine fellow I am, and yet it seems I suffer from a lack of confidence. Still I suppose most people with whom I mix would say that I was mentally superior to them."

As in the case with so many of our patients, this man seemed to have no suspicion of what was really the matter with him. Intuitively he knew that something was wrong, that everything was wrong, life was not right, and it was no good living it in its present unsatisfactory state. Something had to be done. But, as we have seen, when one asked him what was wrong, his answers were most vague and inadequate.

We frequently get patients who can tell us definitely *what* is wrong. Experience shows that they are in truth no better off than this present patient. It is merely that, possibly through less intelligence, they have translated their vague intuition of "something wrong—everything wrong" into a more precise delusion, or a more definite affective state.

Similarly, to explain his trouble, this patient invented the analogy of "toothache," but he had no idea where the "aching tooth" really was. Also, it is noteworthy that his concept of cure was the dentist, one whose job it was to cure toothache mainly by extracting the offending organ.

However, the trouble of which he complained, or the form in which he complained of it, was at this stage of his analysis apparently very far removed from sexual conflict, or from the concept of the "cure" of such conflict by the removal of sexuality.

As he said he read "an enormous number of books," but I have no doubt that he found not the slightest hint of what he was unconsciously seeking in any of these books. Their authors were similarly innocent of the private unconscious sources of human distress, or, if not themselves innocent, they felt that their readers were hardly prepared for such premature interpretations.

If for a moment we put ourselves in the position of the

mediaeval physician who knew little of organic disease and nothing of bacteriology, and imagine a patient with advanced tuberculosis presenting himself and complaining, shall we say, of a pain in his side, of blood spitting, of a febrile state, or even of anaemia, we should not be surprised if the modern tuberculosis officer throws contempt upon our endeavour to cure the particular symptom.

Similarly, if in the course of treatment its form should change from that of pleural pain to night sweats and debility, we should not nurse the illusion of cure or improvement, nor the idea that we are necessarily nearer the appreciation of the underlying disease.

Like the tuberculosis patient, like every sufferer from a psycho-neurosis, the subject of our present case paper presented me with a description of his *feelings*. Be it to his credit that these were a puzzle to him. What did he know of underlying disease? None of the many books he had read, nor their authors, knew anything of it either.

Let us be content in this first interview to observe his creditable dissatisfaction with his endeavours to understand what was the matter with him and with the theories advanced to explain it.

Elaborating his opening remarks, he said:

"I think what I suffer from is a vacuum, or a sort of pain, deep down in my soul. I am like a person with the toothache who cannot discover where the aching tooth is or even whether there is a tooth there at all, or merely a space.

"I have tried to solve my problems myself, but I don't seem to get anywhere definite. That is why I thought it best to come to a person who professed to be able to understand these things."

But perhaps the most relevant thought that emerged during this first interview was:

"I don't feel that I am properly grown up."

He admitted that the *recognition* of this was a sign of increasing maturity.

"I am facing up more fully and more consciously to

the 'something wrong'—this feeling of inferiority. I am prepared to take all pains and endure all practical expense to the limit of my funds and of my ability."

In the course of the routine case-taking of his family history and past history, which is a customary part of the first interview, a few further interesting symptomatic revelations appeared which he had not consciously thought fit to put in the forefront of his symptom-picture.

For instance, it transpired that though he had now reached the age of thirty he had never once been in love. He was not unduly inhibited. He had had several cheerful girl friends. Some of them, or most of them, had liked him very much, but to be quite candid he had never obtained much pleasure from their friendship.

On occasions he had even gone so far as to indulge in sexual intercourse. Strange to relate, he had in this respect been "quite normal," thus confounding the theories of analysts, such as myself, who erroneously assume that persons with any neurosis necessarily suffer from some degree of sexual impotence.

However, unlike many neurotic sufferers this man was exceptionally frank. Having said so much he dropped his guards and defences, "came clean" as it were, and admitted to me:

"Do you know, Doctor, in all these relationships *I have always felt a fraud?*"

I could only reply: "In making that remark you are not defrauding yourself."

Then he related to me an incident which brought his rather intangible psycho-sexual impotence, with the emphasis on the psychical factor, into high relief.

"Last summer," he said, "I took a particularly attractive girl on a boating holiday. We had arranged for three days on the river. The weather was glorious. We were alone in the upper reaches of the Thames on a wonderful afternoon.

"I talked to her for two hours, and then felt my conversation had petered out. The awful thought occurred to me, 'Good God, what am I going to do with her for the rest of the afternoon and the evening, leave alone the succeeding two or three days! Whatever will I find to talk about!'

"I could find nothing. And at the same time I had grown tired of poling. I thought, 'Heavens, hours and hours alone with this girl in the punt!' She did not seem to share my discomfort. She lay languorously among the cushions, carelessly playing with the water over the side. Whatever was I going to do for the rest of the time! Whatever would I find to talk about to keep the party alive!"

Analyst: "If you had consulted your *feelings*, what would they have suggested?"

"I should have pulled up at the bank, made some excuse, got out of the punt, come back to my flat in London and never so much as thought of her again. Anything to have got out of that awkward and embarrassing situation! All I could see before me was hours and hours and days of utter boredom, with nothing to say and nothing to do."

Analyst: "Surely this experience is an epitome of your whole life and of your dissatisfaction with it? But tell me how did it come to pass that you found yourself in such a position with a woman? You must have desired or engineered the situation?"

"Well, I suppose I did it because it is the usual thing to do on holiday in the summer. Most young men would be glad to take an attractive girl on a boating holiday. Perhaps she suggested it in the first place. Anyhow, it seems to me the usual way to conduct one's holiday."

Analyst: "Another question. You are now proposing to spend a succession of hours, albeit with twenty-three hour intervals, lying on this settee in my company. Do you anticipate that you will similarly be at a loss?"

"No. You have told me, and I have read, that my job will be simply to say whatever comes into my mind."

Analyst: "Might you not have behaved similarly with the young lady? You could have lain beside her, and similarly said whatever came into your mind."

"Oh, but that is the trouble. Nothing would have come into my mind. In that first two hours of conversation I had already said everything I could say."

Analyst: "Does it not seem to you that some natural process which takes place in relaxation, specifically in mental relaxation, was under prohibition, taboo or repression? It is noteworthy that this prohibition was begun by the presence of a woman and is relatively absent in the presence of a man, a man older than yourself."

[An explanation of this lack of emotional interest in the girl in the punt will be forthcoming towards the end of Chapter VI.]

In the meantime, with these concluding remarks, we will leave the first interview with this particularly interesting young man. The symptoms of which he at first complained are already seeming to be almost irrelevant to the real nature of his trouble, a trouble which made him feel that life was not satisfactory, which made him intuitively seek the help of a psychologist.

What is the matter with this patient? Is it his hesitancy and his lack of confidence—always feeling that he is not quite grown up? Or is it that beneath these symptoms there is a certain doubt whether indeed life is worth living at all, and if so what is the source of this depressing doubt?

In approaching the question of how treatment proceeds I wished to illustrate in this chapter that it is a mistake to identify the symptoms with the illness.

If we can see only the superficial manifestations of a deep-seated trouble we may try to cure these manifestations alone, thinking that they are the disease. When their shape alters, as it has probably already altered several times in the course of the individual's life, we find that the *form* in which they were at first presented to us has disappeared and we may proclaim a cure as misleading and as illusionary as was our first superficial conception of the illness to be cured.

The matter goes far deeper than this. In every case the most original of all "symptoms" were the manifestations of primary instinctual urges, themselves manifestations of the inherited nature of life itself.

And this is the interesting point. The individual, or even the race, became ill through trying to *"cure"* these. Thus, if we take a similar view and similarly endeavour to eradicate the substitute (symptomatic) outlets for tension which have replaced the original natural ones, far from mending the damage we shall only be extending it *and* by the identical method.

That is why I have so stressed this point. Before we can talk of "cure" we may have to reorientate not only our conception of cure but even our conception of symptoms, disease and normality—and indeed our conception of the nature of life itself.

This patient's case story as it unfolds may help us to begin this necessary reorientation.

Chapter II

A Glimpse of Technique

THE first question that arises after the interview (dealt with in Chapter I) is whether or not Analysis is the appropriate method of treatment.

Whilst it may be a justifiable ideal that every person neurotic, psychotic or normal should be analysed, practical considerations often swing the pendulum to the other extreme. Further, it must be borne in mind that it is sometimes only after a few weeks of testing of a particular case that we can speak with certainty of the progress the patient is likely to make.

The most remediable cases are, of course, those in which the principal symptom is *actual conflict*,[1] and the main source of the illness current causes of libidinal imbalance. But even here there is always a characterological basis for anomalies of libidinal distribution as there usually is for actual conflict; therefore, whilst we may get some immediate improvement, further amelioration may still be hard to achieve.

Any classification of neuroses from the point of view of ease of curability is almost certain, in the light of experience, to be grossly misrepresentative. The therapist is constantly encountering cases in which the presenting symptom raises hopes of a ready cure only to find on going more deeply into the matter that the patient's character, or some psychotic streak, or other relatively hidden trait renders attempts at cure protracted, dangerous or well nigh impossible.

In general it may be said that cases in which the precipitating factor seems to have been of outstanding importance and of recent date, for instance cases of war traumata, are the most readily ameliorable, but experience

[1] "Actual Conflict" may be defined as worry and difficulty in connection with current affairs.

teaches us that every such patient was already suffering from a latent and hidden psychoneurotic or psychotic predisposition, and that his illness, though apparently precipitated by the recent trauma, is really nothing more or less than a release from repression of his previously repressed morbid potentiality. He may improve to a certain extent early in treatment, but may take as long a time as any for successful modification of the foundations of his illness.

In short, every case is a mixture in varying proportions and degrees of every one of the neurotic, psychoneurotic, psychotic and characterological categories, and the proportions in which they are mixed will only emerge during the actual process of analysis.

Therefore we must leave this difficult subject and content ourselves with a consideration of the particular case which we propose to review. He is conspicuously unclassifiable, but his illness, if such it can be called, will take us to the very springs of many psychoneurotic, characterological and perhaps, though to a lesser degree, psychotic illnesses.

There is something fundamentally unsound in a person who having reached adult age is not sexually attracted, or is inadequately sexually attracted, to persons of the opposite sex. We may confidently expect that if left unmolested sooner or later neurotic, hysterical, perverse, cyclothymic or depressive and perhaps even schizoid trends will manifest themselves. He is already feeling doubts as to the value of going on living—a common precursor of a state of morbid depression. If treatment is to be undertaken we must be prepared for a long and exhaustive character analysis.

METHOD OF PROCEDURE

The essential details of analytical technique will I hope reveal themselves more clearly as we proceed with the clinical material, but a few preliminary remarks may be necessary.

In general a patient has been made ill by an attempt on the part of his ego to override his instinctual disposition. Hitherto all persons who have attempted to help him have unhesitatingly sided with his ego and encouraged him further to over-rule his instinctual nature, thus reinforcing not his health but his illness.

The outstanding mistake which all persons, including doctors, not versed in psychotherapy are sure to make is that of a premature attempt to ameliorate the patient's symptoms or even his character.

If analytical treatment is to be adopted the first principle is that the analyst should refrain absolutely at the outset from the slightest attempt at amelioration. He has one object and one only and that is to get the patient to unburden his mind in an ever-increasingly uninhibited manner. Any attempt to modify the patient, or even the slightest criticism of any of his remarks is bound temporarily, or even permanently to interfere with the unguarded freedom of self-expression; and secondarily it is bound to interfere with transference development and so utterly to defeat its own end. One essential principle of therapy must always be borne in mind and that is that it is only by virtue of a successful transference situation that the physician will ever be in a position to effect any psychological alteration. Therefore at all costs the development of transference[1] must be the first consideration. Put as briefly as possible if somewhat inadequately one might say that it is essential that the psychotherapist should be the soul of tact.

This should be transparently clear in most cases. For example, in a paranoid patient the slightest suspicion that the listener is not a party to his delusions, and the confiding in him of these delusions ceases abruptly. Instead of an ally he becomes an enemy to be guarded against, and transference possibilities are at an end—with the possible exception of negative transference and a consequent negative therapeutic result. In this connection one is reminded that negative transference normally sets

[1] Transference is more fully explained on pp. 226-7.

in at that late stage of analysis when the analyst does
finally attempt some modification or frustration of the
patient's psychological pleasure-principles. But at the
outset it is to be avoided.

It commonly happens in neurological hospitals where
the doctors in charge of patients may not be adequately
trained in psychotherapy that the patient pours out his
confidences to a nurse or masseuse, while remaining somewhat on his guard against the physicians, rightly or
wrongly assuming that these latter will endeavour to "put
him right."

The therapist should let the patient tell his story in his
own way, if necessary encouraging him to do so, himself
remaining completely passive and receptive and if possible
indulging in no interruption or curtailment whatsoever.
In addition to transference considerations the physician
should remember that it is only by complete passivity
and infinite patience that he will get an unadulterated
picture of the patient's mental state.

By virtue of the doctor's attention, tolerance and understanding the patient will feel as though he is being loved
and will give his love or positive transference in return.
The positive must come first. Even an infant will not be
successfully corrected by a parent or mentor who does not
love it or whom it does not love. The result of such attempts
is more likely to be neurosis or psychosis than successful
adjustment. Correction is unconsciously interpreted as
hate, and provokes rebellion, hostility and withdrawal
(self-protection, isolation, introversion and schizophrenia),
whereas love alone encourages positive transference relationships.

One of the essentials of analytical treatment or indeed
of any form of psychotherapy is that the analyst should
understand, or at least show a willingness to understand,
the individual psychopathology of all the patient's symptoms, behaviour, thoughts, feelings and even beliefs, his
emotional patterns and his general characterological
structure . . . understand as a mother understands her

child . . . understand as thoroughly as the ideal mother whom the child never had but always longed to have. Only on this understanding (i.e. loving) and uncritical basis can the essential foundation of all psychotherapy be built.

There is one exception to the general rule of silence for the analyst, and that exception is where his understanding is so profound that he is able on the appropriate occasion to give a really *Deep Interpretation* of the superficialities which the patient is presenting. Such an interpretation if not premature, that is to say *if it does not arouse the patient's resistances*, is the one thing which above all else will bind him to the analyst and to a continuation of his treatment. Those who are not sufficiently practised in this art, or who have not a natural genius for it, would be safer not to make the attempt. Technically this is a process of the analyst siding with the patient's id in contradistinction to his previous would-be mentors who have merely sided with his ego.

A FEW GENERAL PRINCIPLES OF THEORY

Certain general principles of theory as well as of technique may be a help and a guide if only for the sake of preserving some degree of orderliness in the physician's mind. Perhaps the most outstanding of these for practical purposes are the following concepts. The Unconscious, Libidinal striving, Frustration, Precipitating Cause, Conflict, Repression, Regression and Fixation. A clear understanding of these is essential. They are defined in the Glossary.

In accordance with these concepts the process of symptom formation may be envisaged as follows:

The libido is conceived of as the energy of pleasure-giving instincts for ever striving for satisfaction or relief of tension. While it is gaining this satisfaction all is well, nervous and physical health is preserved. Frustration of libidinal satisfaction may initiate a process which leads to symptom-formation. But the psyche is often capable of enduring an extraordinary amount of frustration without becoming ill. The sort of frustration which is most likely to lead to illness is an intrapsychic form called inhibition. It can be regarded as resulting from an internal frustration or a psychological inability on the part of the person to deal appropriately with the environment.

Perhaps the essential difference between the normal person and the neurotic is that the normal suffers essentially from external frustrations and so *actualizes* his conflicts in the real world for ever striving to overcome this or that reality obstacle to the gratification of his libidinal trends; whereas, the neurotic finds or *erects* frustrations all around him at every point and gives up the struggle to cope with them on a reality plane, instead retreating from reality into his inner world of intra-psychic conflict. There his libido meets with similar obstacles or frustrations (the external ones which initiated this process being usually the projections or dramatizations of his internal ones on to reality) and his conflict itself is subjected to a process of repression in order to preserve consciousness from the disturbances. The result is that libidinal energy eventually regresses and the journey towards neurosis and symptom-formation has begun.

His libido is no longer driving him forwards against the obstacles of a real world, of real and perhaps conquerable frustrations to its strivings. Instead his libido has regressed backwards along the intra-psychic paths of his previous mental development. Old and no longer appropriate emotional patterns are re-activated and he uses up his energy in a world of obsolete struggles.

To sum up: Environmental frustration produces a check to the normal forward direction of libidinal striving, and the resources of the mental apparatus are called into operation to overcome the frustration in the real world. This is normality: the direction of energy to modify reality so that one can gratify one's desires in relation to it. Frustration becomes a precipitating cause of illness only when this normal struggle with environment is abandoned;

and the libido, no longer moving forward in time and
space, reverses its direction and regresses along the path
of its former development.

Thus we see that the libido supplies the energy for the
symptom, as it does for the process of health and of life
itself.

What determines the clinical nature of his illness and
the particular form his symptoms will take are his *past*
experiences and his past emotional reactions to those
experiences. Where in his earlier life, particularly in his
infantile life, emotional experiences have been most intense and most sustained it would seem as though some
quantity of libido had remained as it were *fixated* to the
emotional patterns then set up.

It is as though these fixation points, as they are called,
act as magnets to the now regressing libido. They become
re-animated and produce a form of behaviour and
emotional experience totally out of keeping with the
reality requirements of his present day life. This behaviour
and these emotional experiences are the symptoms of the
particular illness from which he now suffers.

Thus it will be seen that whatever the reality frustration may have been and whatever the actual or precipitating cause of the patient's illness, its *form* or nature is
predetermined by previously laid down and repressed
emotional patterns of his earlier life.

As these patterns were formed in infancy and during
the earliest years, months and weeks of life when they
were being called into being, developing and passing
through their vicissitudes, it will not surprise us to learn
that the nucleus of every neurosis and the clue to the
form it takes lie in the patient's infantile life and development.

Though elucidation of the patient's actual or current
conflict may produce some amelioration, this is likely to
be slight and transitory unless the relationship is established between this conflict and its prototype, and possible

progenitor, in the repressed conflicts and fixation points of infancy.

Thus anything more than the most superficial and transitory amelioration necessitates a tracing of the conflict down to its original infantile patterns.

This is not such a fantastically difficult task as we might at first suppose, because the pathologically reversed libidinal flow has already traced it for us, and we and the patient have as it were only to follow the libidinal stream to reach these infantile fixation points and sources, now, by reason of the illness, alive and active.

Free Association of Thought is the newly conditioned mental stream to which we turn for aid in this process. It too runs along the libidinal course, along the line of least resistance to pleasure-principle or libidinal trend.

Resistances and defences will arise all along its course, and our main task, if not our only task, throughout analysis will be to remove these obstacles to analytical progress.

Everything that interferes with the progress of analysis is called defence-resistance and a full account of it would be impracticable at this stage of our clinical study as it would involve an almost complete treatise on technique. Whatever interferes with the progress of analysis and with the patient's free association of thought, particularly in the early stages, manifests itself principally in the form of *anxiety*. Hence it will suffice to say the analyst's first duty will in many cases be that of removing initial anxiety so far as possible.

The impression frequently given is that while Free Association of Thought may be classed almost as a form of operation of the pleasure-principle and therefore having a certain libidinal drive behind it, anxiety appears to be its opposite number constantly checking or embarrassing its freedom. Other resistances will, of course, sooner or later arise. These have been classified under various headings such as ego resistances, super-ego resistances and id resistances.

However, the incomparably important resistance to any complete analysis is practically always one which arises automatically and is completely without insight by the patient. This is a special form of resistance called Transference. It is as though the patient's mind tends to re-enact his infantile emotional patterns as though they belonged to his reality relationship to the analyst, rather than exert the necessary mental energy that would be required to convert them into memories of his own early life. It is therefore at this stage of the process that the analyst's special knowledge, insight and skill and his unique opportunities of interpretation and reconstruction will have the utmost demand made upon them. It is for this reason that the greater part of this book on a case of deep analysis has been devoted to the transference situation.

Such is a very brief outline of the theoretical structure which the analyst may bear in mind to give him some sense of system and orderliness in his investigation and procedure. But it cannot be too strongly emphasized that no theoretical structure should be rigidly adhered to or take precedence over the fundamental principle of observing and absorbing all the clinical evidence, including particularly the material which the patient produces in Free Association of Thought. Therefore at all costs the patient's thoughts must be allowed, and if necessary encouraged, to flow with absolute freedom, unencumbered or discouraged or adulterated by any concepts or interference by the analyst.

As soon as we can tactfully induce the patient to do so it is usually most helpful (except perhaps in some manic cases) to get him to lie on a comfortable settee in such a position that he will not be able to see the analyst. The latter sits behind or beside the patient where he can observe without being observed and without any undue intrusion into the patient's thoughts. The length of the sessions is usually fifty to sixty minutes, though this is admittedly an extemporaneous concession to environmental reality and has no justification in the nature of psychic processes. If possible it is best for the sessions at least in the early stages of treatment to be daily, otherwise there is a danger of the patient's interest flagging before a sufficiently important libidinal movement¹ has got under way. To explain the necessity of daily interviews at the beginning of treatment I sometimes say to a patient "it takes more energy to start a vehicle moving than it does to maintain the movement."

Towards the end of his first interview sufficient of this analytical programme was explained to the patient who is the subject of this case paper, so that on his second attendance the conditions of analysis could be immediately adopted. As little as possible was explained to him, as my experience is that a person commonly does Free Association of Thought more freely if his mind has not been encumbered by any unnecessary and often anxiety-provoking instruction.

DIFFICULTIES THAT CAUSE FAILURE

The principal causes of analytical failure may be classified under two headings:

(a) Those belonging to the analyst, and
(b) Those belonging to the patient.

Of the two probably those belonging to the analyst are the more important, particularly if the case has been rightly selected. These include, (1) anxiety, impatience, and other psychological attitudes which cause him to intrude himself, and prevent him from so much as beginning analytical investigations. (2) An absence of psychological flair or understanding so that like the patient he is apt to be innocent of the unconscious sources of the symptoms, life-history, etc., which the patient is telling him; and (3) most important of all, a failure to appreciate the development of transference, most particularly of silent negative transference.

The analyst's remedy is to re-submit himself to a personal analysis.

Those pertaining to the patient include, (1) a constitutional inability to appreciate that his behaviour and psychological affects have unconscious causes; that is to say an unalterable projection of himself into his environment and an accompanying lack of ability to acquire insight. It may be said that this difficulty is conspicuously encountered in all normal persons, (2) Intense anxiety, (3) Psychoses, and (4) Too firm a resistance to transference interpretation.

It may safely be said that the whole process of analysis will be a constantly recurring struggle with all these difficulties. There are occasions when the analyst will have his own difficulties to cope with as well as those of his patient, most conspicuously when the patient's affective life emerges with all its violence in the transference situation.

to allay anxiety—the patient's, not our own, for, unless we ourselves are free from anxiety in this situation, we are not yet qualified to conduct an analysis—and to allow, or if necessary to encourage, the patient to take the initiative. If he does so we are content to listen and say not a word. If he asks what is expected of him, I generally say "just talk," or "speak your thoughts aloud." It is only in a few cases that it becomes necessary to explain to a patient precisely what is meant by Free Association of Thought, namely the process of refraining from exercising any conscious control or direction over one's thought processes and of speaking whatever thoughts or feelings one is conscious of at the moment, without exception and without exercising any selection or choice. Rushing unnecessarily into such explanations is frequently a sign of anxiety on the part of the analyst, and is then apt to create anxiety with its inhibiting effects in the mind of the patient.

If the analyst is free from anxiety and therefore able to refrain from unnecessary speech, to relax his own mind and to reflect upon what he sees and hears, he will from the outset be accumulating understanding of the patient and his at first sight incomprehensible symptom-picture. Let him preserve his resources and his accumulating understanding for an appreciation of the developing transference situation, a detection of it behind its masks and subterfuges, and a complete insight into the infantile pattern which it will endeavour to hide from him. Let him reserve his speech for an unmasking of the negative elements of this transference, for if, for his own peace of mind, he here enters into a conspiracy of silence with the patient, it is not enough to say that analysis will fail, it will simply not take place.

Chapter III

The First Analytical Sessions

At the first interview as recorded in Chapter I the patient had summed up his complaint in these words: "Everything is wrong. Life is not right, and all I know is that it is no good my continuing to live it in its present unsatisfactory state. Something has to be done." He had proceeded to the illustrative anecdote of the boating holiday, and in the meantime he had thought of another instance—possibly as an unconscious resistance to Free Association of Thought.

In keeping with his conscious and effortful pursuit of "normal" pleasure-behaviour, he had taken a young woman this time for a motoring picnic. Everything had been accurately thought out: nothing had been left to chance. Immediately upon the conclusion of the meal he had produced from his car pocket two books, one for himself and one for her. As he said: "So that we could spend the remainder of the afternoon without difficulty or embarrassment."

With no books to read at his session he was reduced to the following Free Association of Thought:

"I noticed a great satisfaction in coming here last time. I felt I had made a start. I felt more sure of things. I had the feeling that discussions with you would clear up my problems. I was surprised because I rather expected to be suspicious."

The word "discussions" caused me a little secret amusement. I was reminded of the letters of a doctor acquaintance who sends me patients with a note referring to my "chit-chat treatment." Apparently those whose unconscious source of anxiety has not been dealt with are innocent of the existence of a deeper mental level. Like this patient, one can say meaningless things easily, but things which have emotional significance are relatively suppressed if not repressed. His anecdotes had given rise to the question in my mind as to whether this young man was really incapable of an adequate quantity of emotional experience, and the correlative thought that if so this was going to be a very serious and difficult case indeed.

Whatever the uninitiated may say about psychotherapy in general and psycho-analysis in particular, the clinical fact remains that most patients under Free Association of Thought and without the slightest interference or question or suggestion from the analyst soon come to the subject of sexuality. Having come to it they remain at it for what may seem to the beginner an inordinate length of time.

The possible exception to this general phenomenon are cases of war neurosis and cases in which the actual conflict at first appears to be the essence of the breakdown. But in these cases it transpires that the usual thought procedure is only temporarily postponed. However, the analyst's policy, like that which he enjoins upon his patient, is to refrain from interference with the natural process of the unfolding of the mind.

Like others this young man soon came to this subject —at his very first analytical session. His attitude to it was so typical, so like that of the vast majority of cultured men and women, that none but an analyst would presume to call it a symptom.

It was simply this: "*Sex is a nuisance.*"

He said: "Here am I wanting to make a success of my life, wanting to be mentally efficient. I have had a magnificent education. I want to make the best of it . . . to go further than my fellow men. I have ambitions to become a great man in some way or another, and every now and again—much too frequently—sex keeps cropping up and interfering with my general efficiency. It is most exasperating. I think I would manage my life much better if I could be cured of this nuisance."

However common among normal men and women may

be this attitude to sexuality, it nevertheless has all the characteristics of a symptom. To begin with it is a "complaint." The person complains of it. Furthermore, its psychopathology is characteristic of all symptom-formation.

I remarked a little earlier that the source of symptoms was always the primary instinctual urges striving for expression and meeting with anxiety and resistance on the part of the ego.

If we ask which impulses go to form the dynamic source of symptom-formation the answer is those which arouse conflict, are not accepted by the ego and therefore opposed, and complained of, by it. And here is clear evidence of such an urge.

If this ego attitude towards sexuality is so universal, it only tells the psychologist how universal must be the raw material or the basis for symptom-formation. Furthermore, this patient, like most patients, does not complain once. He almost filled these his first analytical sessions with elaborations of this complaint, and with comments upon it.

He said: "In proportion to my ambitions and what I expect of myself my life has been a history of failure. My free association of thought to that remark is the history of failure in my sexual life. At fourteen and a half I started to masturbate, and for fourteen years thereafter tried to stop it, only to experience failure, failure two or three times a week.

"That is enough to undermine all one's confidence in oneself. No wonder I am ill and have to come to you. Of course, that failure has led to failure in every direction. Incidentally it has led me to a great deal of introspection. I am always thinking about myself. I am not sure of myself, not sure of anything.

"After fourteen years of introspection I am still wondering how much one should be oneself and how much one should control and regulate one's actions. It seems to me it must be all a question of degree or balance, and

I do not quite know the degree. I have not worked it out, and if I do work it out I do not stick to it.

"It seems that a little imp within me says, 'It would be a fine thing to break the rule you have made.' What bothers me is this impishness that breaks in and makes me break my self-discipline. Or do you think I ought to forget all about self-discipline?

"I believe it is all mixed up with my struggle with masturbation. When at school, I would make the most solemn pact with God that it would never occur again, but it always did. I am stuck at the sexual age of sixteen. One part of me makes rules and the other side breaks them."

Here we got a typical sample of the advantages of Free Association of Thought. The patient's mind immediately reverted to some memories of childhood whose link with his present thought was a similarity of emotional charge or pattern. He went straight on to say:

"When I was a very little chap, less than three years of age, the woman scrubbing the floor told me to be careful not to tread on her fingers. I immediately did it. It was a sort of impishness, or meanness. I think I had some idea of getting my own back. They must have been crushing my will and I would interfere with their will in order to get my own back.

"I took a delight at pulling out drawers and letting the contents crash on the floor. Later I used to play water games and flood the bathroom. I know I was beaten quite a bit, but I cannot tell whether I was beaten because I did these things, or whether I did these things because I was beaten. In any case I must have had my will broken.

"Is that why I was no good in checking my masturbation later? Or was it the same conflict going on between some impish impulse and the authority that wanted to punish it and stop it? Do you think perhaps that I am still a little child, still with all the uncertainty of that age, still giving way to impulses and still being beaten, but this time by some part of myself?"

Perhaps it should be mentioned that it is no part of the

analyst's function to answer the patient's questions. This
is obvious if the patient continues, as did this one, without
waiting for an answer. If on the other hand the patient
demands an answer to a question and waits for it, it is
usually safe analytically to invite him to answer the question or himself to invent the answer which he thinks the
analyst might give him. He is thus kept from reversing
the roles of analysand and analyst. In this case the patient
continued without a pause.

"I think as a little boy I felt they had won. I seem to
think now that I felt 'Let them have their own way. I
am beaten.' Perhaps it is on account of that feeling which
I had at an early age that I cannot put up any determined resistance now. If some strong-minded person
insists, I have to let him have his way. Perhaps that is
why I try to get allies in advance. I have no proper
confidence in myself.

"Of course, though I am telling you all this it is the
last thing I want other people to know or to suspect.
Above all things I want everyone to think I am a man
and a great man at that, or if not yet a great man I will
be one. At times I want to think that myself.

"Probably it is on that account and for no other reason
that I have occasionally, though very rarely, even gone
so far as to indulge in sexual intercourse with a woman.
I think I must tell you that my psychological behaviour
in this respect is probably very different from that of other
men.

"I do not think I have ever really *wanted* a sexual
relationship. I do not like the idea of a woman's body
in that respect. It does not appeal to me. In fact, I am
not sure that it is not positively distasteful. Nevertheless,
I have done it. During these relationships my chief mental
concern is a sort of introspection as to whether I am
enjoying the act or not enjoying it.

"I have not the faintest conception what the woman
is experiencing. But the main anxiety in my mind is
whether I am doing it as well as everybody else. I am

chiefly concerned regarding the problem of my supreme ability. It is just the same when I am writing letters. I am in a flap all the time lest it is not the marvellous letter that Chris Martin would have written."

This reference of the patient to himself by name further arrested my attention. I remembered my friendly talks with advanced cases of schizophrenia in various mental hospitals. I remembered the morbidly-introverted and reality-withdrawn young women, often sitting in an odd posture, with cold, rigid and blue extremities, who have said to me: "*She* did not sleep very well last night."

If one asks "Who is she?" they reply, "She, the child." They are referring to themselves.

Their choice of the third person is an indication of their extreme emotional dissociation or schizophrenia. This patient had given considerable evidence of some degree of such dissociation in addition to this fortuitous reference to himself by name. Nevertheless, unlike these other cases he had a sufficient abundance of ego to make him not an asylum inmate but a valued and moderately successful member of society, and, moreover, one who recognizes that he is not quite satisfactory.

It helps not at all to label his illness "a form of Obsessional Neurosis." The smug satisfaction we achieve by arriving at a diagnosis may deflect us from our real purpose: that of understanding and curing.

He continues: "I rather despise my desire for showmanship, but I do so want to be the right sort of person and to make a success of my life."

The trouble with this man is unfortunately that he is not getting the guide for his conduct and success from instinct sources. Perhaps it is because his repression of instinct, dating from an early age, has been too thorough. Has he as it were dropped the propeller of the ship of life? Has he immobilized or cut off the source of compulsive energy necessary to any and every form of success? It must be because he has repressed his emotions.

His ego has entered into conflict with his instinct life

and repressed it so violently that he has in some degree split his psyche. The split may be only slight, but it is nevertheless most serious. Defence against emotion has at some very early age been only too successful.

If we rob life of its very springs of action what can we do to enable it to continue a satisfactory course with sufficient impetus? His trouble is that having immobilized the horse, the source of his dynamic energy, he is now trying to pull the cart *himself* (ego), and moreover, to pull it better and more effectively than all his competitors who have their teams in full service.

His case is not the exact parallel of the asylum women. They have immobilized, they have bound up, all their id-horses and substituted nothing in their place. The ego, or driver, is also immobilized sitting on the horses' heads or bound up with them!

In our patient there is a difference. His ego is free, very free and very active. It must be remembered that developmentally the ego is a specialized part of the id and only later takes over the function of opposing in some degree its parent instinct-system. It appears that in this particular case the compulsive energies and urges, organized in the id in the form of instincts, are still active, very active, in the ego.

If the driver has tied up his horses and forgotten them, he has certainly not tied up himself (his ego). Here our metaphor breaks down. We must revert to psychological terms. The tragedy of the condition is this: the ego cannot successfully substitute itself for the id because *the meaning of life resides in the latter.*

The id created life, and it is the id which continues to give it not only its health but its energy and its drive, using the ego, despite the latter's frequent opposition, as a tool or servant for its (the id's) purpose.

Moreover, it is the id which provides life with its *meaning*, albeit unconscious, and with its satisfaction.

Even a dog, a wild animal, or a child (who have not studied the wisdom of man nor visited medical psychologists) are satisfied with life and do not question its meaning.

The "wisdom" (unconscious wisdom) of the ages resides in the id. If this has been bound up, repressed, no amount of activity on the part of the ego will be a satisfactory substitute. The ego may borrow its compulsive energy from the id (for example in compulsive or obsessional neuroses), but evidently it cannot borrow its meaning and its power of achieving satisfaction.

It redoubles its energy, compulsively striving to manage life on its own. It fails because it has to a great extent divested itself from contact with the reservoir of unconscious wisdom. It looks to other egos, perhaps equally sterile, for help and guidance.

This patient says: "I read a lot of books. I must have a plan for life. I must map it out properly. Sex must be excluded, must go by the board. Success is what I want."

But then he shows a little doubt when later he asks the question:

"Should I try to be a great man, or should I just be content to be myself; and if the latter, where is myself, how can I find him?"

And there is his fundamental self, his instinct life, just beside him, and, if not completely tied up, at least separated from himself (his ego) by a chasm over which only a few inadequate bridges remain.

In this psychic construction he has "solved" his earlier problem, if indeed this can be called any sort of solution. We may ask the question, "What induced his ego so to immobilize the 'horse,' or id, the reservoir of instinctual urges and affective feelings?"

It seems that the answer to such a question must be that his ego was so frightened of the severity of the super-ego (analagous to parents who administered the beatings, but infinitely more harsh and terrifying than they could ever be) and consequently so terrified of admitting into consciousness the forbidden instinctual impulses, that, with almost superhuman effort, it immobilized these latter and endeavoured to take on their function itself.

Therefore, he must *plan* things. Life must be conducted by his ego. In no case may the id or instinct be listened to or permitted to come to his aid. He reads books and plans things so that his ego alone may be his guide; but an ego without an id is like a government without a people. It has no strength or substance behind it.

No form of ego activity can reproduce life, and no ego deprived of id drive can maintain in health the life which has been produced. That is why the young women I referred to in mental hospitals have cold and even blue extremities; even their circulation is beginning to fail. In their case competence to deal with the realities of social life and even of nutrition have already become utterly bankrupt.

This is illness indeed, whether it be with or without tangible symptom-formation. In fact, the roots of it are so deep that one is justified in wondering whether they can have their origin within the span of one individual lifetime, or whether indeed they may not be the advanced products of a morbid process which set in generations ago.

The problem of cure is not the simple procedure which the uninitiated would assume it to be. The roots of disease, like the roots of health itself, are part of a life process of age-long continuation in which the identity and independence of the individual is more illusionary than real.

Nevertheless, although development may tend to be in the direction of accentuated morbidity, it is conceivable that it may also be deflected in the direction of removing morbidity which has already come about.

If we can initiate a movement in this latter direction we have at least begun a process of amelioration.

Chapter IV

The Beginning of Transference

F ROM the fact that the patient presents us with no startling symptoms, neither of a mental nature such as the
usual list of phobias and compulsions, nor of a physical
nature, such as the innumerable multitude of hysterical
aches, pains and dis-functions, it might be assumed that
his illness is not so bad as that of the majority of patients
with whom we have to deal.

This would be an entirely erroneous conclusion. Our
deeper knowledge of psychopathology shows us that his
predicament is far worse than that of the average psychoneurotic, hysteric, or obsessional. I shall indicate why.

In every case of psychological illness, and, I am inclined
to add, at the initial stage of every physical illness, no
matter what symptoms present themselves, the fundamental source of the trouble is conflict—conflict between id
forces or between these on the one hand and the super-ego
or ego forces on the other hand—conflict in which the
dynamic energy of the id, prevented from its original
natural mode of expression (by instinct activity), and
coming up against opposition within itself or with super-
ego or ego forces, has no other course but to express itself
in some alternative form, usually one which is opposed
to the interests of the ego. This product of the conflict
is called a symptom.

Now, in the particular case which we are here investigating it will be seen that the impulses emanating from
the id do not get even this much symptomatic outlet. It
is as though they got as far as the super-ego only and are
there lost, absorbed, paralysed, so that they never reach
the ego or any form of external expression at all. Thus
it appears that conflict, the source of symptom-formation,
is in this patient at a minimum. Apart from a lack of

awareness of his own wants and desires, apart from a consequent state of indecision when he is thrown upon his own resources, he can hardly be said to have any symptoms at all. Nevertheless, there is one thing, and one only about which he is sure, and that is that he requires help.

The absence of all overt symptoms coupled with the fact that he hardly finds life worth living suggests to the analyst the most serious of prognostic indications, because it would convey to him that the conflict had already been won by the forces which oppose health, well-being and life itself. That is why we can see so little evidence of the battle; but evidence there is, not that of the noisy guns of hysteria, nor the backward and forward swaying of the struggle which we detect in a typical case of obsessional neurosis, but merely as it were that of the piled-up dead lying upon the battle-field. And we cannot believe that the ego, however competent to deal with the shadows and symbols which comprise the so-called realities of our conscious life, we cannot believe that this ego is unimpaired.

In short, the psychologist will detect that *this man's whole personality is the symptom*. Further, he will detect that of all cases which present themselves for treatment this will surely be the most difficult to cure.

The patient says: "I suppose the chief reason why I come to you is that I am not satisfied with myself. I am not satisfied that I am satisfying myself in life. Perhaps it is that I do not feel that I have achieved anything worth while. Sometimes I think it is because I am haunted by the need to become a great man.

"I have had a wonderful education, taken the best degrees at the university, and read an enormous amount, and, as compared with the people I argue with, I have reason to think that I have a first-class brain. And with my interest in sociology and the social structure I feel that I should have qualified myself to become a cabinet minister. In spite of all this I do not seem to get anywhere at all, and every now and again I am haunted by this idea of becoming a great man.

"It is difficult to define what a 'great man' is. I am rather at sea about it, not quite knowing what I should do next. But since coming to you things seem to be changing. Yesterday I realised that it would be much more fun to be just *me*; to do what I wanted to do.

"But there again I seem to be a bit stuck. I am certainly not at all clear what I do want to do. Perhaps it is this woman business that is wrong! So far as I can see other men seem to know what they want in that direction: though God knows *how* they know!

"I feel that I ought to be as sure as they are about these matters. *That* must be where I have gone all wrong. We must investigate it.

"For example, I will tell you the way I approach a person of the opposite sex. First of all I think, 'What does she think of me?' And after I have wondered about that for a very long time I next begin to wonder whether she would think enough of me to allow me to be intimate with her. Then I feel that I am over-reaching myself straight away.

"Perhaps some anxiety comes up there, because my next thought is: 'She is probably just the same as all other women, so why bother?' However, I do seem to bother. I cannot let the matter rest. And, before we have really got to know each other, I make some suggestion to her which she invariably refuses.

"Now I come to think of it, perhaps I do this on purpose to make sure that she *will* refuse; because then I can say to myself: 'Oh, well, Chris, you cannot manage a woman!'

"You see, this goes on because otherwise I would not know what to do in the situation; I'd just be bored stiff. But this way I manage to work up a little stimulating anxiety all the time, because, in addition to the burning question of what she thinks of me, the thought at the back of my mind is this: 'Good Lord! Suppose she fell for me! Suppose she wanted me to be intimate with her!' I would then have to put it off somehow, and that might be very awkward or difficult.

"Of course, if she asked me to stay with her to the end of my life I'd know what to do. I'd simply bunk. In fact, as soon as I have started any emotional interest I am frightened and do run away. Yet, on the other hand, I expect all women to fall for me, and if they don't show it I am resentful, and I think that they don't think anything of me.

"There was that instance I told you about when the woman expected everything of me. I just panicked. I got all sorts of worries and excuses. I think I want the *idea* of it all, but am frightened of the reality. But it is not the fright of the impotent man. It is a different sort of fear; or, at least, it takes a different form.

"So, you see, I am all in a muddle. I am made like a man and feel I ought to behave like one. But when it comes to the point I am bothered about how I *ought* to appear before women.

"I asked a fellow once, and he told me to pretend to her that I could not live without her; but, apart from the ethics of such a technique, I know that if I attempted it I'd burst out laughing in the middle. Still, my anxiety suggests to me that there is something I more or less can't live without. And this effortful love business, however successful a show it may be, does not seem to supply what I want.

"I feel a sort of conscious gratification that I have made the grade, as though I had struggled through a difficult examination paper, but the conclusion I come to is that *it is such a sweat being a man.*"

At a subsequent session the patient began as follows:

"Your remark at the conclusion of our last meeting relieved me of a lot of anxiety. You said: '*Perhaps you don't want a woman at all.*' How obvious! I wonder I didn't think of it before! I *should* have done, because I had been coming round to the idea that it might be more fun than being a man to remain just *me*; to do what I wanted to do."

Analyst: "What would you want to do. What would give you pleasure?"

Patient: "That is where I seem to be done. I don't know. I don't seem to feel any strong desire for anything. It seems to me that I have always had to decide what I would like to like, and the only pattern I have been able to take is that made for me by other men and their likings. I suppose that is why I have driven this woman business so far.

"Now I come to think of it, it was much the same at school. The other boys of my age liked playing ball games, so I tried to like it too. What a mutt I was! They thought I ought to be good at it because I was so strong and full of energy. But my only impulse on the playing field when the ball came towards me was to get away from it. Nevertheless, just the same as at this woman business I had to put up a show.

"So the problem, even on the rugger field, was rather complicated. It amounted to this: How to get *away* from the ball and yet at the same time give the impression that I wanted to get *to* it. Ah well! Now I see that copying others is no good, and will never tell me what I really like, however much I would like to like it.

"So you ask me what I would like. Let me think. I think I like dancing—romping around to the music.

"I once said that to a girl who was a beautiful dancer, and she looked at me with undisguised contempt, and then roared with laughter. Perhaps that damped my ardour a bit. Though I don't think I was ever really very keen; it was just because other people did it. Maybe I'd enjoy myself just as much running up and down the stairs.

"Well now, what other inclinations have I got? I like reading when there is nothing else to do . . . and there usually isn't, except work, which, incidentally, I may say I am very good at. I particularly like reading biographies: the lives of distinguished old gentlemen. I have done a bit of writing myself, you know; I wrote a series of articles once on 'How Best to Occupy One's Spare Time.' I had got it all fixed up, because I felt that one's spare time ought to be planned out, so that one did not just waste it."

Analyst: "Suppose you did just what you like doing?"

Patient: "I'd be completely at a loss. I immediately begin to think of what I would like to like. So there again, I start planning it out. So far, as a result of coming to you, I seem to have reached the conclusion that many of the things I would have liked to like, such as women, I don't really like at all. I only give myself a lot of sweat and anxiety.

"I am stopping all this nonsense now that I have come to you. I think I will become clearly confident; you will be able to guide me."

Analyst: "Now you are putting the onus of planning your likes and dislikes on me!"

"Yes, of course. But one must have some advice regarding the problem of how to enjoy one's life. Otherwise how should one know? One might do the wrong things and get all wrong."

Analyst: "You are asking me to 'hold the baby,' and to decide for it what is best; and probably to do for it what will be most comfortable."

Patient: "Yes, that is what I am doing."

Analyst: "Why? What is the idea?"

Patient: "That is the way I will get out of the responsibility, the need to think out for myself what I do not understand and cannot think out. That is the only way I can get rid of this mental effort. Then and then only will I be able to relax."

Analyst: "Is not this rather reminiscent of your earlier life?"

Patient: "It is identical. It is the day-dream of the only child. That is what I want to get back to. If you will take over the guidance, or more, that is what I can get back to."

Analyst: "In short you want your daddy and mummy back. Perhaps you never wanted to leave them."

Patient: "Yes, I suppose the truth is that I didn't want to be a man."

Analyst: "If one has not grown up naturally to be a man, one tries to make one's ego or reason, in lieu of the parents, take up the task for one—as it were, to take the place of the absent father and mother."

Patient: "I can see that that is what I have done all my life. At school I was always too sensible or too old. I can see now it was because I was emotionally too young and therefore had to compensate for it by being intellectually above the people I was emotionally beneath. That is why I was always over-efficient. I see now that it was an ego-efficiency, gained at the expense of discounting one's feelings and substituting constant effort and stress."

Analyst: "How early was that?"

Patient: "I was sent to school at three and a half. I felt my deficiency very early, and got this idea of competition. I had to be better than the others. I am still either terrified of people older than myself, or else (and this is a trick I have learnt better as I have grown older) I make them into 'fathers.' But I was always eager to get home to my real father and mother; and now I can remember the feeling I had in doing so.

"The feeling was more than one of relaxation, it was a feeling that I could now be a baby again. I see now that it is only when you have that security that you can grow naturally. The school did not provide it.

"I am wondering now whether my parents provided it, or whether they simply took over the business of living for me in the same way that I want you to take it over. It occurs to me that when I have planned to put on clean underclothes, that is on a Monday morning, it has always been an effort for me to put them on. It seems such an enormous task that I can hardly manage it. I feel sure it is because I have not got mother to shove me along. I feel now that if mother were there, telling me to do it, I could do it without difficulty.

"That is the same sort of role that I want you in. I think throughout my life everything I have done was done simply and solely to please father and mother. All the positions I have got in life, the very profession I have adopted, have all been to please mother, instead of what I wanted to do to please myself. In looking back it seems to me that all I could ever think of wanting to do was to please mummy.

"I find it difficult to see that other human beings can be fallible. I have a tendency to feel that all other human beings must be 100 per cent all right—infallible like the Almighty Father. Mother seemed to want me to be like this, that, or the other, and it would not occur to me to think she might be making a mistake regarding what I might like best.

"So I come to you, and ask: 'What do *you* want me to do?' You say: 'What do *you* want?' and I say: 'I don't know: what do you advise?' Whenever any elderly person advises me to do anything, I seize on to it, and go ahead, and try to please them."

Analyst: "In the thrall of the parent image!"

Patient: "You ask me what pleases me. I don't know, because I have always been pleasing the parent. I wonder if I really do want to be what I am. My first thought is that I am pleasing the parent and at the same time pleasing myself but not knowing it. My second thought is that I am not pleasing myself after all. This applies not only in work; it is the whole structure of my life."

The above is an excerpt from an abundance of material that continued throughout several of the subsequent sessions. The patient was constantly referring to instances of the emotional emptiness and bewilderment of his present-day life, and associating them with identical emotional occasions which had existed in his earliest infancy, and which he now remembered with increasing conviction and vividness. But in due course he seemed to have worked through the greater part of this material.

Eventually the day arrived when he opened his session with a particularly interesting remark. He said:

"I have nothing to say."

After a few minutes of silence I asked him what he was conscious of. But I put my question in these words:

"How do you feel?"

He said: "Very comfortable."

Analyst: "You like it?"

Patient: "Oh! You are referring to the way I am lying on the settee? Yes, I often want to roll up in a ball and be comfortable, to feel that somebody is taking care of me. The thought is of my childhood, when I would like to go home and be fussed over. I like lying here. I don't want to go away and deal with anybody or anything."

When a patient in the analytical situation feels "very comfortable with nothing to say," we can be sure that the transference situation has arrived.

What do I mean by "the transference situation"? I mean that he has arrived at a stage of his analysis when he is repeating his forgotten emotional feelings and experiences of childhood, of infancy, and even of baby-hood, in the present day within the analytical hour using the analyst as a substitute for the parent, and actually feeling as though the analyst were the parent, and he were again a little boy. This is the eventual situation which it is the task of analysis in due course to interpret and to make conscious to the patient. It is within this period of his emotional development that the nucleus of all his conflicts lies—and more than this, of all his emotional patterns and of his personality itself.

Lest the reader should deem that this little excerpt from this session is inadequate evidence upon which to base such a far-reaching contention, we will take the session a little further.

The patient apparently thought it enough to reveal that he was conscious only of feeling very comfortable and hoped to be left undisturbed to enjoy that experience of comfort. However, I asked him to exert himself just sufficiently to give me his Free Association of Thought to that comfort and its postural expression. He said:

"I feel that it is just like going back to my cradle—into a nice little warm place."

Some analysts would seize upon this opportunity to interpret the "warm place" as mother's womb, but I do not feel that at this stage of analysis this would be the wisest procedure. However true the interpretation might be, it would be emotionally meaningless to the patient.

He might at an intellectual level agree with it; but, even if he did so, a resistance on the emotional or unconscious level to such an interpretation might well interfere with the progress of the analytical transference situation, and the most modern analytical technique is a strategic development of that transference situation; that is to say, the avoidance of any remark or behaviour which might interfere with this dynamic tendency of the psyche to reproduce the infant situation, using the analyst as the parent-surrogate.

Subsequently, of course, when the situation has been fully developed it will be a part of the work of the analyst to interpret it completely and fully, whether the patient likes it or not. But this time is not yet ripe.

However, the encouragement to do Free Association, rather than to lie and sleep, had aroused the patient sufficiently for him to continue the analytical process.

He went on to say: "I don't really want to go out into the world and be tough and rough. I'd rather be a little child; as a child you can put your ideas out; you can just say what you like. You don't have to trouble to differentiate between the good and the bad ideas, or even between good and bad people. It is much better just to accept people, to accept them as daddies and mummies. It makes the world much more comfortable.

"I should like a woman to do everything to me—a great, big woman to come and look after me and satisfy me in every way, bending over me and looking after me.

Then I would lie back and take no trouble, and make no effort—go off blank and have no thought at all."

Analyst: "How old are you?"

Patient: "About eighteen months."

Hence his concept of the administering woman being "great" and "big." If one has gone back to the age and presumably the size of eighteen months, mother must indeed be of enormous proportions.

We are all familiar with the humorous figure of the little man with the big wife. It is not only traditional, but also topical. The little man in Tommy Handley's "Itma," who says, "I would do anything for the wife" has a *big* wife and the humour of the situation is obviously that of the baby-man and mother-wife relationship.

Contrast with this the common preference of so many men for an undersized woman, despite its racial disadvantages. Is this a reversal of the above tendency instigated by incest taboo, a flight from the mother-image?

Compare, too, Charles Baudelaire's (1821–1867) French poem *La Géante*. The relative size of mother and babe is emphasized both by patient and poet:

> J'eusse aimé vivre auprès d'une jeune géante,
> Comme aux pieds d'une reine un chat voluptueux.
> Dormir nonchalamment a l'ombre de ses seins,
> Comme un hameau paisible au pied d'une montagne.

Translation:

> Beside a young giantess I would love to have been
> Like a voluptuous cat at the feet of a queen.
> To sleep tranquilly in the shadow of her breasts
> As at a mountain's foot a village rests.

Chapter V

Regression to Infancy

In the last chapter we left the patient lying on the analytical settee curled up in the position of a babe in the womb enjoying the phantasy that he was again in the cradle relieved of all the responsibilities of life, with a great big woman, a mother-imago, bending over him and ministering to all his needs. By means of this regression all the problems of life had been solved.

It was suggested that this was the transference situation, namely that the patient had transferred his emotional pattern of infancy, apparently of the first few months of life, into the present day, the present moment of his analytical session, and that if he were not already using the analyst in lieu of a parent-figure he would soon proceed to do so.

Before coming to a conclusion we may safely await events. For a considerable time the patient continued to show a preference for his early emotional life and an objection to or resistance against assuming the role and responsibility of the adult.

He said: "I have got the body and the appearance of a man therefore I am expected to behave like a man—but *what a sweat!*

"It is a question of what the world expects of me and what the world is prepared to accept from me. To hell with the world! If I consult my inner self I find there is a fundamental feeling of inadequacy and purposelessness. All that is put right if I go back to childhood. The feeling then is: let daddy and mummy run everything for me then all my problems are solved.

"Sometimes I feel: if I can't be a baby perhaps I could feel like a woman and say to myself 'my husband will decide that for me.' So I come here and lean on you. But you are not very satisfactory, although I must confess a

D

few sessions ago it seemed that you were—or perhaps it was that you were going to be. There is still some hope that you will do it all in spite of your not having come up to scratch so far.

"My instinct is to lie here and *suck your brains*. I am greedy. I think now of all the books I have been sucking in for years, feeding myself up as it were, and growing or trying to grow at the expense of older people's brains."

Analyst: "You are still a greedy baby."

Patient: "Why shouldn't I be? I am following my secret heart; but now I think perhaps my instinct will let me down. That reminds me of my fear of heights. Perhaps it is that instinct *wants* to fall.

"As a child my instinct was to use my left hand, but these dreadful adults wouldn't let me. Instinct said 'there's your left hand—use it.'

"But no, I was not allowed to, I had to do something different, different from my instinct. I was made to use my right hand. That is why I became unsure of my limbs, and am still a bit unsure about them and about everything that is me. So that was the first step in robbing me of my confidence."

These remarks, like dreams and symptoms, tell us a deep truth wrapped up and disguised in a superficial untruth. Ego values have been substituted for id ones. The truth is that it was frustrations of his libidinal nature that made him unsure of himself and robbed him of his confidence, in short, that had a "castrating" effect. The untruth is that it was essentially this particular interference; it was not; it went deeper than this.

The patient continued: "The second [step in robbing him of his confidence] was when I could not do Latin and French. I was very good at Mathematics, but they would make me peg away at the Latin and French. I never got anywhere. I only lost still more confidence in myself. In fact, I think it was through educations such as these that I have gradually lost myself altogether. And now I have got to come to you to find myself. And what do I find? A baby in a cradle!

"It seems that I want you to repeat all the old errors of my upbringing when I ask you to give me guidance. It is all this blessed guidance, or misguidance, which I have had since birth which has caused me to lose myself.

"I have been wondering how politicians say the right thing promptly. It must be that their instinct does it for them. I may say that I have been strikingly successful during the last thirty-six hours in my practical work and in everything else—more successful than I have ever previously been. I see what it is. People will get as far as their instinct carries them and no further.

"If your conscious mind tries to make you greater than your instinct or to get you further than your instinct will take you, you get a failure or a breakdown. That's the explanation for the nervous breakdowns which happen to these moral reformers, and even I believe to psychologists.

"I have been rather excited about my own success during the last couple of days, but I would like to go back to where we left off last time. I felt I was in baby clothes. It was so delightful."

Psycho-analysts will say that this patient's libido (instinctual pleasure energy), having met with frustration on the mature genital plane has regressed to the very early fixation point of infancy and the very early infantile voluptuousness of genital-less dependance on parent figures. It only remains to add that the frustrations initiating this regression were the particular effective intra-psychic ones. Their pattern will be seen later to be that of parent-fixation with its repression of genital-sexual conflict. Such interpretations were not given at this stage.

His voluntary attempt to repeat his previous transference session, relating to the earliest months of his life, was a failure—another instance which shows us that transference, like everything else within and without analysis, cannot be ordered by the ego.

Admittedly ego-resistance can *postpone* it, but, fortunately for the success of analytical treatment, it cannot postpone it *indefinitely*, provided the patient attends regularly and does Free Association of Thought.

There was something else with which he was unconsciously or instinctively more concerned at the moment, and that is what occupied the session. It was instigated by the anxiety which inhibits the free indulgence of the pleasure-principle. The anxiety could be briefly expressed as follows:

"What sort of a man is this whom I am with? Is it safe to indulge in Free Association, to let myself go utterly in his presence?"

A full transference situation rarely develops without this inhibiting anxiety coming out and being dealt with. He was not going to plunge further into the transference without due caution and protracted reality-testing.

First I was treated to a harangue about the nature of "Truth." How can one distinguish truth from falsehood, fact from fancy. What "yardstick" has one to measure these things by? The material was reminiscent of much that one reads in the well-known philosophers. Similarly it led nowhere.

It was just a symptom, an important symptom of anxiety, and might be interpreted thus: "Is the person to whom I am proposing to surrender for the sake of ease and comfort, is that person mother or father—or an enemy?"

Or we might go further and say: "Is mother (or father) wholly benevolent? Is it safe to surrender?"

Every analyst knows that it is not for him to enter into any discussion on the conscious plane. His work in the analysis is simply to allay anxiety, preferably by its interpretation. Therefore in reply to his questions as to how he was to distinguish between truth and falsehood I said:

"The ego has not got to choose. Perhaps it need not bother."

Patient: "I can't think of anything to say."

Analyst: "See how sterile the ego is!"

Patient: "Yes, I see, it is just sitting down on the id."

But soon he found plenty to say. It was as follows: "Have you got any children? What are your religious beliefs, if any, or do you believe in spirits?"

As I did not so much as attempt to answer he continued: "I can't help wondering what your religious beliefs are."

And then, in exasperation: "But it is damnable! I can't get anything out of you."

This, particularly in the light of recent material, could be interpreted as his annoyance at not being able to suck anything out of the breast.

He continued: "I can't talk till I know you as an individual." (Interpretable as unable to perform his physiological functions unless mother will see to him.) "I can't adjust what I say to suit your mood." (This remark shows the inadvisability of the analyst displaying any of his own thoughts or beliefs or moods.)

"You are colourless—clever but colourless—no assessment of your personality is possible. I am always doing that with every person I meet and I have been coming to see you for weeks and I might never have met you for all I know of you as an individual. A man who knows the very guts of me!

"I would like to tear you down and be at you. I can't even find your private address in the telephone directory. What is your background? Do you eat?" And then, soliloquizing: "Perhaps he has no personality to know, no personality at all."

So long as the patient continues to do Free Association of Thought there is little need for the analyst to interpret even his anxiety. Everything that enables the analyst to remain a colourless background or a blank slate upon which the patient can, and eventually will, write his own emotional patterns makes for the clarity of the analytical picture that will ensue. His phantasy is left unadulterated and free to express itself.

Presently it will be seen that he is increasingly impatient

for the analyst to take an active role in the proceedings
and inclined to become exasperated at his persistent
inactivity. But with all this the pleasure-principle, on a
mental plane the principle of Free Association of Thought,
shows signs of winning in the struggle.

He says: "After last session I had the feeling that the
hard resistance was beginning to break up. That feeling
has continued. How long it will last and how you will
wind it all up I don't yet know. I fancy that you will
point to the high lights and fit it all together. But I do
get a bit impatient sometimes. I think: 'It is all right for
him (the analyst) to say "this is useful material," but isn't
it time he began to push in an idea now and again?'

"Surely it must develop to a stage when you will take
a more active part. All the activity so far seems to be on
my side. Incidentally, I may say that this applies more
than previously to my life outside this room, also. I tele-
phoned a girl friend of mine the other day and I was much
more natural than usual. But it is chiefly you I have been
thinking about.

"I suppose it is because I can get nothing out of you
that I picked up one of your works the other day and
tried to see what I could learn from that. I suppose I was
really trying to learn what I could about you, trying to
get something out of you as you are so blessed hopeless
in this room.

"I did get something. I felt tremendously stirred, had
to put it down after a while. I wish you would be like
that here with me—positive, definite, instead of so con-
foundedly impotent."

(A person under analysis is discouraged from reading
psychological books—not excepting those of his analyst.)

It is quite usual for every patient at some stage or
another to wish that the analyst would adopt an active
and potent role so that he, or she (the patient) could lie
inactive like the baby in its cradle and receive all the
blessings heaped upon it by the benevolent parent imago.
In spite of the analyst refusing what might to him be the

self-gratifying temptation to fall into this desired role, the patient nevertheless cannot resist the tendency of his libido indefinitely, and will play out the little drama, if necessary all by himself.

This particular patient was no exception to the rule. He finally gave up his resistances and plunged into the natural emotional phantasies of his childhood pattern.

Once this initial resistance had gone the stream of his libidinally charged thoughts and phantasies swept him vigorously through several months of progressive analysis.

"Perhaps I am three-and-a-half or five. I stopped growing at that age. Perhaps my character is a childish character. I am not a man as I should be. I am really a child at heart although there is a generous covering of apparent adulthood. What are you going to do about it?"

Analyst: "Are you asking me to carry you around?"

Patient: "Yes, but I don't want you to really. My father used to carry me about when I was very small. It gives me an incomprehensible little catch in the throat when I say that."

Analyst: "Then he died and you lost all and so you came to me."

Patient: "You won't do it."

Analyst: "I am no good."

Patient: "You are a flop."

"All I need is a rattle and I shall be a complete baby again. It'll be such fun to come in and rag you. Perhaps you would take some notice of me then. For instance, I would come in with a sucker in my mouth and you would rush into print! Or come in on all fours barking and you would say, 'That's very interesting'—and it wouldn't mean a damned thing at all."

Analyst: "You would be forcing me to play your game."

Patient: "Yes."

Analyst: "Still it would be your game."

Patient: "I suppose it would, but not to the extent I would like to make it."

(Silence.)

Patient: "I am being just a nasty, sulky little boy today, saying 'No, I won't do it. I won't smile. I won't do anything in the chamber. I will be obstinate.'

"I had a dream last night. I had better waste your time by telling you that. In the dream I was in a hurry to come and see you (God knows why). Two women I knew were with me, Mary and Magdalene. (Both have attracted me sexually.) I got into your consulting room, but it was nothing like this; it was your ordinary home with books and furniture all around—dark, old-fashioned furniture. We were walking round the place and I was showing them how an animal—a sugar-bear as I called it—rolls about and as I rolled on my back doing a somersault act you came in. I felt it was a pity that you had caught me behaving like a child."

At the next session he bounded happily into the room and then made this astounding revelation:

"I had a temptation to come here and act like a child, to do somersaults on the floor. I was so keen on the idea that I even put a jersey and short socks into my attache case. I had the idea of doing a quick change in your waiting room and when you opened the door I would come in here with a teddy bear and a box of bricks and toys and a pad of writing paper and just be a child and play trains round the couch."

Though this patient is, on an ego level, obviously making fun of his analyst, that there is nevertheless some genuine id tendency to regress to childhood is revealed by his tireless protraction of the "game" and by the material which subsequently emerges.

He continues: "But then I thought: it is enough to *tell* daddy that. And then I thought that today I was going to buy a toy engine and bring it in and start it off on the floor here and go round and round the couch on all fours after it like this."

With that this large man rolled off the settee and proceeded to crawl round it saying "Chuck-chuck" and

puffing his cheeks out pretending to be a steam engine.
"I wondered what you would do. What are you going
to do if I just go on crawling about the floor doing chuck-
chuck?"

Analyst: "Suppose I just sit here."

Patient, having resumed his position on the settee:
"Then I lie on my tummy and try and write with my left
hand. I cut myself with my penknife and cry. Then I get
cross and say '*I won't do it.*' I knock the bowl of water
over and see if I can get any reaction from you—I just
want to be a child of four or five, and I *still* want
to be.

"I want to play trains. I want to roll about the floor
and do somersaults; such fun to bury one's head under
the couch and to find broken springs and marbles and
nuts and bolts from the Meccano set; draw a house and
funny little people under the house; sharpen my penknife
and cut my finger again and cry; and then have something to suck.

"I would write and draw things with a ruler. I would
be looking up at you to see how you were taking it because
I would want your approval, or at least your attention.

"I giggled to myself last night. I don't know whether
it would be a good thing because you might just disappear.
One's always anxious as a child testing one's mother, a
little afraid lest one goes too far and she disappears. Still,
you want to know just how far you can go without her
disappearing.

"You might say, 'That's not the way to behave Chris.
Lie on the couch.' I would say 'I won't.' Then I would
do it again and knock over the vase of flowers. I'd try to
draw and feel the difficulty, difficult enough with either
hand. Perhaps you could tell that if you tried to draw with
your left hand, but when I was made to use my right it
was practically impossible. Anyhow, it's great fun trying
all these things. I like being like this."

Analyst: "For ever?"

Patient: "In the end I would get tired and lie down

here and go to sleep. But if you told me to go to sleep before I was ready I would kick and yell.

"I think now that I'll write to Father Christmas. I thought Father Christmas was silly at three or four. He was dead at five.

"I want a nice appreciative father to watch me play and tell me how to play. I would have to have some sort of dog, or doll or pet animal. It would be jolly good fun to sit down and be one's age and just roll about on the floor."

Analyst: "Were you deprived of this as a child?"

Patient: "I played whenever I wanted to, but I expect I missed somebody looking on, and there was no one to play with. Still, its nice to roll on the floor and get one's legs stuck under an easy chair, or lie on the floor and kick one's legs in the air. *You* won't fiddle or fidget. You don't understand the pleasure to be got from doing it."

Analyst: "Parents don't understand."

Patient: "Yes, that was it. There was no companionship for me. They never understood I didn't want to play the piano; but I did want to write and they couldn't understand that—the silly twirps! Everything was lost on my parents. I just wanted to be with somebody like me, erecting scaffolding all over the house. This is the period of my life which I return to naturally.

"I thought yesterday and today that I *could* go further back still . . . further back than games and toys. These are already only a substitution. I could go back to playing with toes and other bits of one's body instead of toys. And later I may say one goes back to those earliest things quite naturally. The toys fail one in the end, or perhaps they don't fail entirely. We still have trains and aeroplanes.

"I can see now that one goes forward from playing with one's penis and things like that to playing with toys; and later, much later, returns to the first one—with a difference—in the same way I suppose as one starts with a woman (mother), then leaves all that for many years, only

to return in the end to, again, a woman. And in the
absence of the woman it is indoor games with oneself.

"I wonder if I will want to masturbate again after
analysis. Should I masturbate or not?"

Analyst: "It depends if you want to relieve your tension
by masturbation, or endure your tension in order to relieve
it by analysis."

Patient: "I feel that the only way I can solve my problems is to go on being a baby, holding mother's hand,
reaching up to it and expressing wonder at everything
around me. 'Mummy, why do they have lamp posts?'
I don't want to be a man a bit. I want only to make funny
little grotesque remarks, and Mummy would look after
all the things that mattered. I really feel I want to be
about two and a half, just seeing life for the first time."

Similar material to that given here occupied a large
number of this patient's sessions at this stage of his analysis.
It was no doubt part of the phenomenon of the transference
in so far as it was a re-living, or at least a pretty vivid
remembering, of the thoughts, feelings and phantasies
which had occupied his childhood life and built up his
emotional patterns from that age.

What concerned his analyst was the question whether
he had remained unduly fixated to that age, and if so what
had interfered with his natural emotional development.
Had the process been interfered with from without or
had something happened within the psyche to occasion
this repression and to prevent healthy progress to maturity? What was the precise nature of these happenings,
when did they take place, and would he be able to
remember them?

I may say that although we had not reached the point
of being able to answer these questions, the time is not
wasted in allowing a patient to do Free Association of
Thought, particularly if these thoughts are concerned
exclusively with infancy, for what may seem to be an
unduly long time. Within a few weeks of the emergence

of this childhood emotional material he was saying to me:
"The influence of the analysis is with me all the time.
I am not at all self-conscious now as I was before I came
to you. I can never again be so overwhelmed with difficulties or so depressed as I have been in the past."

Even if this is not strictly true, it is an indication that
some improvement may be in store if Nature is allowed
to do her work without obstruction.

Frequently cases that improve most under analysis are
unaware of the precise mechanism responsible for the
improvement. On the other hand, the ego, or intelligence,
may be amply gratified by receiving answers to all its
problems on a conscious plane and yet the patient's
symptoms may remain untouched.

Thus we see that analytical progress is not identical
with intellectual satisfaction, but, like health itself, may
be something totally independent of it.

This theme will be developed further in the next chapter, together with even more striking evidences of the
patient's regression to the emotional patterns of childhood
and a very dramatic proof that he allots to the analyst the
parent role in these fundamental character-constructing
experiences.

At the same time some insight will be gained into what
is actually responsible for initial analytical improvement.

In the meantime I would like to conclude with a
delightful little German poem which brings home to us
the great pull which these early experiences have upon
us all, even in their undisguised imagery. It is called
Homesickness (*Heimweh*) by Klaus Groth, 1819–99. It may
be translated as follows:

> Oh, if I knew the pathway there,
> The dear way back to Babyland!
> Why, to seek fortune, did I e'er
> Let go my mother's hand?

Oh, how I long to rest, nor rise
With any need to strive or chafe!
Only to close my tired eyes
With love to keep me safe!

Never need any effort more,
But dream so easy and so mild,
Heed not what hours rob from our store,
A second time a child!

I sought for Fortune but in vain—
Lost on this dreary Strand!
Show me that dear way back again,
The way to Babyland!

Chapter VI

The Father-Fixation:
(*Its Emergence and its Working Through*)

THE ANALYST is not usually wrong if he assumes that any improvement in the patient which is not accounted for by insight or genuine emotional progress is due to some unconscious satisfaction resulting from the patient's emotional relationship to the analyst himself.

A philosophical theory of why a positive transference relationship improves a person's emotional or nervous health and appears to give him a new and adequate incentive for living, in exactly the same way as does the identical phenomenon of falling in love, might run as follows: In spite of our physical separation from the parent root which occurred with the cutting of the umbilical cord, the mind is never really free from its original physical and mental dependence upon the roots and trunk of which we are at the most only a branch. Our physical separation enables us merely to substitute other roots and trunks for the one which gave us birth, and from which we have, after our almost full growth of nine months, been severed.

Some persons, such as this patient, cling more than others, in an unconscious if not conscious sense, to the parent stem, but the most that any individual can do in satisfaction of his heredity, history and nature is this miracle of substitution of one form of root-dependence for another form. Without this in any form he is dead or dying. With inadequate roots he is ill. The half-cut cord does not provide him with adequate incentive for living. His mental sap has been reduced to a sub-minimal quantity necessary for health.

As soon as he forms a new attachment, for instance towards the nearest parent-substitute, the analyst, as this patient is now doing, his health is automatically improved.

The therapeutic task will be ultimately to free him from the parent roots, even if we have in the interim to substitute the analyst, and in due course to free him from analytical dependence when he is strong enough and mature enough—not to do without any roots, but—to perform the normal operation of placing his roots into fresh territory, when a new tree will arise.

In short, from loving (and hating) the parents he will love (and hate) the analyst and finally love (and hate) a suitable life-partner. It appears that the first part of this process is now under way. He is becoming emotionally dependent upon his analyst, and with this dependence feels his health largely restored. The sapling has reinforced its roots.

If this is so it is a matter which will sooner or later require adequate interpretation if only to free the patient from a childlike dependence upon his analyst.

That this unconscious situation was at the basis of our patient's previous illusion of improvement is amply revealed by the most dramatic transference situation which subsequently emerged, which completely overwhelmed all the patient's relatively unemotional play-phantasies, and which descended upon him like a black cloud which he had never supposed existed in his apparently blue and playful skies, and which left this adult man sobbing like a child not only during his analytical session, but even for some hours between sessions.

The events which led up to this very definite emotional stage of analysis accumulated slowly.

In spite of having luxuriated for so long in the atmosphere of the nursery floor and subsequently having analysed a succession of interesting dreams (which incidentally may have been produced by the patient in such abundance to act as a buffer between himself and his emotional relationship to his analyst), this type of defensive material suddenly broke down and he arrived at one of his sessions in a truculent but more adult mood.

He said: "B . . . this analysis. To hell with it!" (This

remark, startling though it sounds, has classical analytical significance as may be subsequently discerned. The very fact that it is almost too disturbing to be published merely underlines the intensity of its emotional charge in the universal unconscious.)

His next remark was equally surprising.

"You see, I feel pretty good these days. I feel able to stand on my own feet, and this coming here every day leaves nothing else in my life. There is no colour to my life except working and coming here—and I feel well."

Analyst: "Then why come?"

Patient: "Well, I am not quite sure that I am *really* well enough. All I know is that the analysis is an interferer. I am fed up with it. I am fed up with you."

Analyst: "Are you fed up with what I am doing to you, or are you fed up with what I am not doing to you?"

Patient: "I am fed up with what you are not doing. I feel I ought to ask you what I should do during the day. I want a course of discipline."

Analyst: "So you are not really quite well enough. Your first remark suggested that you had achieved manhood and were fed up with the father figure, but now you reveal that you are fed up with not having a father, fed up with me for not acting the role."

Patient: "Yes, that's the part of me that says I am not really well enough to leave you. There are two opposites at work within me, one that wants to get rid of you, and the other which comes to you and says 'Please help me, Daddy.' "

The patient came to his next session in an unusually chastened frame of mind. It was not so much what he said, but the fact that his remarks and his manner seemed to indicate deeper emotional feeling.

There was for the first time a ring of pathos in his voice: "I want to love somebody, but I don't know how to do it. This emotion of love does not seem to hit me as it should. I feel a little resentful again coming to see you.

You are making me into a filleted haddock, and I resent it.

"Or I could put it this way: I am like an oyster that is nicely closed up with all its emotions, all its tender parts inside, and you are prising the thing open. Why should I let you do this? All sorts of disturbances may come out."

Analyst: "You could go away and keep your oyster closed as you have done for these thirty years, but the fact that you came to me suggests that you did not find that state of affairs quite satisfactory."

Patient: "I came to analysis because I felt that this isolation is an unsatisfactory state of affairs. In life I experience alternative enthusiasm and lassitude. I think the lassitude follows because the enthusiasm is always about some intellectual, ego or conscious thing—like the game of a child. It does not lead anywhere. It is an illusion that one has got something good. It peters out, and then I relapse into my lassitude and depression.

"You see, there is no *real* enthusiasm, no overwhelming emotion. I think what emotions I have are just make-believe like a game. They can't last long. But then the question comes to me 'Am I on the right lines at the moment, or is it best to remain self-centred, protecting one's susceptibilities like an oyster that is closed?'

"It seems to me that most people have not got the same clever protection that I have. They just wait until their emotions are upon them, and then they are convulsed, overwhelmed by them. How awful! Don't tell me it is better to be like that. The idea almost frightens me. So far I have succeeded in being emotionally detached from all such disturbances. I am like a potato, complete under its skin."

Analyst: "But seemingly an unhappy or unsatisfied potato."

Patient: "Yes. That is why I came to you. Perhaps I expected you to reinforce the strength of the skin. But it seems to me you are doing the opposite, weakening it

E

and tempting the potato to burst out, to break through its protective skin."

Analyst: "You have invented a very good metaphor for yourself. A potato intact in its skin refusing to sprout! A potato that refuses to undergo the transformation that naturally comes to any healthy potato. What will nature do with a potato that refuses to sprout, that refuses to be transformed?"

[Strictly speaking it is not good analysis to so much as hint at a theory, particularly a far-reaching philosophical one even if we protect ourselves by putting it in the form of a leading question. My excuse here is that my remarks had primarily the analytical object of encouraging the patient to relax, to do Free Association of Thought, and thus to allow the "nature" within him to give expression to itself verbally while he lay on the settee.]

The patient continued: "I suppose there are only two alternatives; either the potato will sprout and be overwhelmed by the forces within it and be no longer a potato but a plant with leaves and flowers and roots and many potatoes, or else its skin will harden over it and it will shrivel up and die. Who shall save his life will lose it, and so on, I suppose.

"Well it may be that I shall come to your analytical philosophy in the end, but I am not ready yet. You see I have managed to achieve a certain equilibrium and I am not disposed to accept an upheaval. The only question in my mind at present is whether or not it is less dangerous to stop nature's forces. It seems that a potato can't, but in the case of a human being who has successfully struggled against sex for fifteen years or more it becomes easier to continue holding nature back."

After a brief silence the patient remarked:

"I am wondering whether one day I shall burst into a flood of tears in this room."

Presently he added: "I have a feeling that I want to cry. God knows why."

At his next session he remarked that he had been feeling flat and depressed. "I still have that feeling that I want to cry."

Analyst: "What would you be crying about? What is your association of thought to this feeling?"

Patient: "I would say perhaps it was because I felt very lonely, the world was an awful place, and I had got forced into a pattern that I did not really want. I expect that I want to love and be loved, but I don't know how to. Now I am thinking about the old crying in my childhood. My trouble was that I couldn't cry properly. It was not free, it was a feeling round my throat—a gripping of my throat, not an open sob, more a strangled cry. My crying was a *hurtful* process because I could not do it naturally."

Analyst: "Perhaps it was the resistance that made it hurtful."

Patient: "Yes, that's it."

Analyst: "Could you compare it to nature in general? Resisting your natural impulses and emotions in life might make life itself hurtful."

Patient: "Yes, it would, that is my trouble.

"And now what you have just said makes me want to cry. I feel that I am being overwhelmed. There's something that I can't control. I might have resisted it out of pride. I don't know what it is. Somehow I feel in such a state of inferiority to you. The steady way you talk just gets me. You make me want to cry. I am just beaten. I feel completely in your hands."

Analyst: "What is the association of thought to that feeling?"

Patient: "Childhood—when one has been browbeaten, found out. One's little artifices have been laid bare; the whole thing is known."

Analyst: "And then?"

Patient: "Mother can't trust you any more. One is let down and crushed.

"For some reason I am thinking of the time when my

father died. One cried when one thought about it and that went on and on until one made up one's mind that one would not cry any more. I wonder if it is that I am hopelessly attached to my mother! I would not feel it if *she* died."

Analyst: "What about when your father died?"

Patient: "I want to cry."

Suddenly he bursts into tears and is allowed to lie sobbing loudly on the analytical settee for several minutes.

Analyst: "What a difference between your reaction to the mother dying and father dying!"

Patient: "Of course there is a difference. (More sobs.) He was such a nice fellow and I liked him. We talked together. I understood him and he understood me. I used to talk to him. I don't know why I want to cry about him, but I just do."

(More sobs, and then he burst into hysterical laughter.) "It is so funny to want to go back all those years. It certainly hurt a lot at the time.

"His dying buried it all, buried all my emotional life. All my capacity for emotion, whatever there was, it was buried with him."

Analyst: "You have not been happy without him, and so you have come to me."

Patient: "I have always got on well with men old enough to be my father, and I have little or no use for any other sort of person. I can't get out of wanting a sort of senior person all the time."

(He again lapses into crying and sobbing.)

Patient: "I don't know what I wanted. I wanted a senior person. It was such a dirty trick to take it away like that. Now I have got to hang on, all on my own. He is the only person I really loved. I have not had his love for twenty years, but the memory must be still there, still retained. I suppose I have been in love with my father all these years.

"The *idea* of being in love with anyone and it arousing an emotional feeling in me! But I suppose it is. (Sobs and cries.) This must be the real test. No, I can't say what I am feeling; I only know I want to cry.

"It must be rather fun to like anybody who is *alive* like that. It is so easy to be a boy of ten or twelve and to like one's father, but to transfer it to someone of one's own present age that would be so different, so difficult. The other day in the light of my analysis I looked at a woman of about my age and thought about her. I saw her patting her hair, and I thought 'to love a thing like that, how ridiculous, how inconceivable!' "

The next day he said: "I felt very relieved when I went away from here last night, but I had not done with my crying. I cried a bit on the way home, and I cried in bed too. It seemed the most natural thing to do. It didn't hurt either."

Analyst: "What were you crying about?"

Patient: "I was thinking what good friends my father and I were. We did nice things together. It was there really that my affections were, *and when I buried him I buried the whole lot.*

"I was left to get on with the person I don't care for. I was jealous of her for having my father, and I was suspicious of her. I never realized till last night what an awful lot I had missed through my father dying. He taught me to make things. I realise now that my life has been a hectic hunt for fathers. Though I have said that before, I have never *realized* it before.

"I had a dream last night. I dreamt that everything was getting into place. The office was being reorganized. It was all being put right, and I was putting it all into place. I felt when I woke up that that is the analysis going into place, it begins to make sense. Here at last we have got some feelings greater than the conscious me. Now it all makes sense.

"I did not want to be bothered going through a lot of explanations about how it fits together. *I just know it does.*"

The analytical developments that had led up to the

patient's regression to the emotional age he was at when his father died had been heralded by some sessions of considerable resistance. In fact, he had played with the idea of breaking off his analysis for good. No ego reinforcements had been brought to bear in order to encourage him to continue, and before any interpretation had been made he himself interpreted it as a desire to "kill off" all father figures as he had already "killed off" all mother images.

In the light of these recent events it seems pretty clear that this independent and truculent mood was nothing more or less than a resistance to the natural tendency of his libido to regress to the age when he was utterly dependent upon father. He was reluctant to re-experience the agony which the father's death, at just that time, caused him to suffer.

However important the revelation and the re-living of those distresses (with the emergence of the repressed emotions connected with them) may be, it is certainly by no means a satisfactory termination of analysis to leave him at the emotional age of ten or twelve.

He will not attain a satisfactory manhood by a destruction of father-images for the sake of a successful resistance to the return of his repressed father-love and dependence; for the repression of this, the most developed pattern of his emotional life, entails an exclusion from consciousness of all his innate capacity to react emotionally to any and every human being. Now that the reservoir of bottled-up emotions has been tapped, it is necessary, for his nervous health, to allow it to flow into consciousness until there is no need for further repression.

At his next session he said:

"I accept the fact that I am in love with my father and it has been this peculiar quality that makes me all funny inside. It is not exactly tummy-ache, it is just a thing that I have no control over.

"I used to tell him a lot of things before he died. I

just said everything that was in my mind. I used to hop into bed beside him. He tickled me and I would yell with delight, or he would rub his prickly chin against my face and I would scream. His death was a dirty trick." (Starts crying.)

"He never warned me at all. Just one Saturday—dead! Like that! If I had known that he might have died it might have been different because then I would not have had all my eggs in one basket. I could not put all my eggs in your basket however nice you are. You are awfully nice. I like you terribly. You are awfully like him." (Here he starts howling and crying all over again.)

"You have such a nice way with you." (Howls and sobs for five minutes.) "But that would not make you him, however much I howled about it. That companionship! That lovable person!

"It is so funny, I can't visualize *what* I was loving then when I was ten. I can't tell you how you are like him, but you are. That nice chuckle of yours, that nice look, that nice way. We could do such nice things together: pull the communication cord of the train, laugh at everybody else—tell me the reasons for everything, why it was such a good idea to work with one's books; be a big brother in a way."

(Here the patient starts howling again and making an unusually loud noise in the process.)

"You see, that made it so marvellous. There was always that response so that I could talk freely. Enthusiasm so that I could talk about anything. Now I have completely buried it all. I feel much better." (He stops his crying, but presently he starts again, alternately crying and speaking.)

"We could try practical jokes to play on mother, and make railway trains, and all my ideas were good ideas, and if they weren't he would show me, and he had such good ideas. My feelings have always been back with that lost daddy. He could not possibly be wrong, so of course

you could not come up to him. He had such a nice way
with him." (He starts crying again and continues to do so
for a considerable time.)

"I am thinking now of when I was at school and the
master sent for me and said he had some sad news that
my father was dead—and that my mother was waiting
to take me away.

"I could not realize it at first. But when I saw my
mother we both burst into tears. That silly woman, my
mother, wailing all the week! And every time I thought
of his death I burst into tears.

"And then finally she said, or friends said, 'Daddy would
not like his boy to cry, he must be a man and look after
mother.' So after a week home from school I went back
and decided 'I will not cry.' So I buried the crying with
him.

"I returned to school in time for evening chapel. I said
'I shall never cry again'; from that time onwards I never
did. I only thought of him impersonally. From henceforth
I was just one of those odd little boys whose mother was
a widow."

At the next session he said: "It seemed so long since I
was here. So nice to be back again. I know I sobbed a
lot. I just feel pretty blank really. I have been thinking
of my father quite a lot. I remember that the first time
I masturbated was in the room where my railway was and
where I used to play with father. And it was when I was
trying to make a truck without him for the first time that
I first masturbated.

"I have had some dream about having a tooth out. The
dream seemed to be that I could keep the tooth and the
pain or I could have it out, but in either case I would
have a tough time anyway. You see I have suffered great
loss and never faced it. I have buried the whole lot, and
buried my life as well, with it. I don't feel I shall ever want
to masturbate again. I see the reason behind it in a way
that I have never seen it before.

"If daddy had been alive I would have been putting a barrier up between him and me every time I did it. But as he was dead I was doing the reverse, that is, I was making another tie between him and me. The result was that the love for him which might have died, the underground fire, was instead freshly kindled for each masturbation.

"*Life as I saw it did not fit me because I saw men loving women instead of children loving their fathers*, and the more I was in love with my father the more difficult it became to have any relationship with women—except the obvious physical one. For me it was like this: I masturbated because I wanted to renew my love of daddy, and of course that meant that there was not any desire to love women.

"It was a fixation to daddy. That was my love-life, and I am stuck with it. But now I don't want to renew my love of daddy in that particular way. If he had been alive my sexual growth would have tended to separate me from him, but through his being dead it tended to unite me more with him.

"All this comes out of some dream that I had which I can't remember clearly. It had something to do with a sexual relationship with you.

"My problem was: instead of it being daddy *or* sex, it was daddy *and* sex. Love of a woman would have meant a loss to me, a further loss after my father's death. My love of father and my sexuality became all one, but of course it was all underground. The love could not be more perfect, because he was dead and my imagination could have it all its own way and make it just as perfect as I required. That was my love-life, and up till now it has all been unconscious."

The foregoing material may give the reader a brief insight into what is called in analysis the "Inverted Oedipus" situation. Inversion means that the sexual impulse which should normally be directed towards the opposite sex becomes instead linked with a person of one's own sex.

There are probably a large variety of causes for this phenomenon, the mechanisms of which are commonly very deeply unconscious.

Regarding the present case this much may be said: the pre-pubertal love of a boy for his father is a quite normal and healthy thing, and if psychologists call it homosexuality it is certainly not homosexuality in the popular and legal sense. Like the love of a boy of the same age for his mother it is obviously pre-sexual in the ordinary sense of the term.

To reach a normal development of post-pubertal sexual life two psychical operations are necessary. The first is that the love for the parent of the opposite sex should have sex added to it, and the second is that at the same time this sexuality, simultaneously encountering the incest taboo, should become diverted to a substitute, that is, to a person or persons of the same sex as the sexually pro-hibited parent.

Now at the age of eleven or twelve our patient was emotionally very much more attached to his father than he was to his mother. Between the time of this attachment and the patient's pubertal sexual development, the father died. All his longings for the dead father presently became reinforced with the development of sexuality and its sexual longings.

There was no material, or real, father to present this developing unconscious phantasy of complete union with reality difficulties and moral taboos. The result was that his love for father, now no more than an image, was consummated with phantasies of full sexual union.

The whole constellation, being so utterly foreign to his ego development, became completely repressed from con-sciousness. The emotionally disturbing memories of his father, and of the agony produced by their contact with the realization of father's death, had already undergone considerable repression. This new constellation of feelings therefore reinforced and added to the repressions already experienced.

The result was that a large proportion of this man's emotional life and all his emotional potentialities were locked up, locked away from accessibility to consciousness, and from their utilization in the world of reality, or even of conscious phantasy and conscious thinking. His sexual life was as it were in a separate compartment, something that operated apart from his conscious psychical levels, that is to say it was unconnected with any conscious capacity for loving, and this latter capacity was impoverished by the absence of the dynamic energy of the sexual instinct.

Though he was capable of physical sexual outlet he was, in consequence of this unusually great repression, incapable of *psycho*-sexual experience in the full sense of the term. The nearest he could approach to it was in his love of another man older than himself in the image of his father. But such a whole-object precluded the possibility of *sexual* outlet as his ego and its censorship would certainly not have tolerated any overt homosexual relationship.

Thus his psyche was split. Sex was one thing and, quite apart from it, appreciation of any whole-object, that is to say any person as such, was limited to father-images. He would rather have spent a summer's afternoon with an intelligent, elderly gentleman than in a punt with an attractive young woman.[1]

Neither one nor the other direction which his emotional needs tended to take could therefore be permitted free or adequate expression. The nearest he had ever got to such adequacy of expression was in his experience during Free Association of Thought lying on the analytical settee. That is why he was in this position instead of in the more normal one of marital love.

This is the degree of elucidation of his psychopathology at which we have arrived at this stage of his analysis, but we are yet to learn that there are deeper and earlier stages

[1] See the incident recorded in Chapter I.

in the course of libidinal development which still remain to be tapped.

I shall not say more about these at the moment than to let fall a hint that before the infant acquires an emotional attachment to its father it is not unusual for it to have developed a very considerable degree of love for its mother.

If such a state ever existed in this patient it had certainly shown far less evidence of its existence than is usual, both in real life and in analytical revelation, and it may therefore be presumed that it was even more deeply repressed and unconscious than that of his much-resisted father attachment.

Chapter VII

The Almighty Father

In the last chapter we witnessed the release from repression of a quantity of love which the patient had unsuspectingly attached to the image of his dead father and which had carried with it fairly complete repression from consciousness of the whole of his emotional potentialities.

We witnessed several sessions and even interim periods between sessions in which this great masculine-looking man had sobbed his heart out in experiencing the return of his forgotten and repudiated love-life. It appeared that such a state of affairs had been enhanced through the death of his father at an age when his boyish love for him was at its height.

At the time of this attachment and before the patient's pubertal sexual development the father had died. All his longings for the dead father presently became reinforced with the development of sexuality and its sexual longings. There was no material or real father to present this developing unconscious phantasy of complete union with its reality difficulties and moral taboos.

The result was that his love for father, now no more than an image, was consummated with phantasies of full sexual union. As the whole constellation was so utterly foreign to his ego development it became completely repressed from consciousness. In consequence of this repression he had grown up incapable of *psycho*-sexual experience in the full sense of the term.

This is the degree of elucidation of his psychopathology which we had arrived at up to the conclusion of the last chapter.

Thus we see that the patient's psyche is faced with the dilemma of whether to love the father image (e.g. successors of the father) with the aim-inhibited and idolized love of his boyhood, at the same time repressing all sexual tendencies, or whether to accept the sexuality which his pubertal development subsequently tends to unite with this father-image idolization.

The latter "solution" which would amount to overt homosexuality is, as I have indicated, intolerable to his ego development, but nevertheless it takes place though its operations are limited to unconscious phantasies. For, at this particular unconscious level of his mind, this is what is happening, unknown to himself, whenever he indulges in masturbation.

To make this relationship to the father image rather more simple one could say that he is faced with one of two alternatives, either to love and idolize father images, at the same time repressing all sexual relationships and limiting his sexual life to masturbation, or whether to regress to the perversion of homosexuality.

The first is sexually unsatisfying, the second is unacceptable by his ego. At this level of analysis it appears that this is why he is so completely bewildered by life and can find no satisfactory solution to it.

The material is becoming unrepressed and we observe him in the subsequent sessions thrown from one horn of this dilemma to the other. The one is sex-repressed idealism or perhaps more accurately a partial sublimation of sexuality in the form of idealism, and the other (which explains the effortful striving after the former) is homosexuality.

In the following sessions we see him clinging to the first in order to avoid the second and endeavouring to sublimate it into religious feelings.

He opens with the following dream:

"I dreamt I was with the prime minister and he said to me: 'I take an interest in that man because I discovered even in school that he is going to be a great man, and I hope that he is. He is very disdainful and fed up at present and he has no friends.' I said it is probably *because* he is going to be a great man that he does not fit in. He said 'His name is Gormy.' "

The patient immediately began to puzzle about this word 'Gormy' which to him at first meant nothing, but he left the subject in favour of a reference to school. He said:

"In school I was always two years ahead of my age and in spite of that the bright boy in the class. I was usually first with all the answers. Of course, I got the idea that I was destined to be a great man—great on the ego plane I suppose you would call it, because here I am lying on your settee and though I am disdainful of my colleagues I am nevertheless fed up with everything and I have no friends in the true sense of the word.

"I have consoled myself with the thought that that is because I am destined to be a great man, that that is why I do not quite fit in. I have not entirely relinquished my ambitions; I may yet be a great man. What I cannot make out is what is wrong with me. In school I used to jaw such a lot that at one time they nicknamed me 'Jawy.' Jawy ... Jawy ... now I have got it! Gormy, that is General Montgomery.

"It all comes to me what I read about his speech the other day. He spoke of religion. We have never discussed this subject of religion, Doctor. I do not know what your beliefs are. I am very anxious to find out, but you are so unsatisfactory. I do not suppose you would go so far in your psychology as to say that all religious beliefs, like everything else, are founded upon some infantile need. Still, I think you might help me by giving me the benefit of your conclusions."

Of course nothing could be more disastrous to an analysis than for the analyst to accept such an invitation.

The patient continued: "Now, General Montgomery, he really seems to have solved the problem. He feels that God is behind him all the time. He knows what to do because he has put his trust in God. What a marvellous solution. He is never alone. He can achieve things just because he feels that he is leaning upon the Almighty Father. I can understand that. That is what we all ought to do. It is a most satisfactory solution for all one's problems.

"Now I come to think of it even in this dream I was with the prime minister. Perhaps that is why it was such a satisfactory dream. I felt sort of buoyed up by his presence. I suppose just like General Montgomery feels himself buoyed up and capable by being on the side of God. He goes in for prayer so he is never alone.

"Now can you offer any better solution than this? After all, all our tests even of the value of philosophy are pragmatic. If it works, it is good, and General Montgomery's belief certainly works. With God behind him he has chased the Germans and Italians right across the African Continent. Can you do better than that? I do not think so. Either you must believe in God or else you must be God, or you are no good to me."

Analyst: "And what are you?"

Patient: "Well, in the dream it seems I am destined to be a great man, but it also seems that I have not quite got there yet."

Analyst: "Are you destined to be the prince of a great king, or are you destined to be the king himself. I fancy there is a difference."

Patient: "Yes, I see that. There is all the difference in the world. It is a totally different psychology. If you are a prince, however great a prince to however great a king, you still do not shoulder all the responsibility. You have someone to lean on, someone to appeal to. You need have no anxiety as long as you are loyal to him. He will look after all that.

"By God! I see it—you are just the son of your father. You are still a son however great you are and however great the father. It is a totally different situation from that of being the father himself."

Analyst: "What is the son?"

Patient: "One who has no sexual rights. The father has all the rights, all the power. He supports you, and you have the compensation and the consolation of being sup-

ported. That has been my role in life hitherto. That is
why I do not get married. That is why I do not fit in the
social life, in the matrimonial life. There is no woman for
me. I am still looking for a father.

"Perhaps, unlike General Montgomery, it is my total
life. Perhaps he has dissociated his into two parts. In his
work he leans upon the Almighty Father, but not necessarily in every way like I do. That is why I am here lying
on your analytical settee more interested in you, in spite
of your inaccessibility, than in getting on with my own
life.

"I am looking for a father, an Almighty Father, in every
sense of the word; and how they all love me, men older
than myself to whom I pay respect! I have never grown
out of being a son. I suppose none of us does really.

"The organization of society consists of a constellation
of fathers ranging from one's immediate bosses to ministers of State, prime ministers (as in my dream), kings or
presidents, to heavenly hierarchies. I suppose all men, all
human beings born as children, insist upon having
parents in some form or another until their dying day.
They are not comfortable without them.

"That is all very well. My trouble is that I have done
this job too thoroughly, too consistently. I suppose most
people do at least escape from this closed system in some
respects, in their sexual life for instance. I have not succeeded in doing so. That is why I am lying on your settee
worshipping the father instead of sitting by my own fire-
side, that is to say on my own throne, with my wife in the
opposite chair.

"I could not bear it. I do not see the sense in fettering
oneself up in life to one of these hair-patting women. To
me it is ridiculous. There is no sense in it. And yet it
seems I do not fit anywhere. I am not entirely happy
alone. I must have a father-figure, a great man to lean on.
I have never got over the loss of my father. I am still
seeking him.

"I suppose you would say the mistake I am making is

F

that of seeking him in the flesh. It is only his spirit that I require. Perhaps I had better give you up and take to religion. What a solution it would be to me if I could really believe that the Almighty Father was always at my side!

"How does one manage to do that? I am afraid that I would suspect that His voice was only the echo of some portion of my own psychology. It would be no good. It would fail in my case. That is why I am in such a helpless position. That is why I am here. That is why I read all these books written by great men, hoping to read in them the voice of the Father. How can I ever usurp his throne and be the great man referred to in my dream? I do not know. It is for you to show me."

Analyst: "It depends entirely in what sense you want greatness. If you want greatness of ego achievement you get it in the same way that any schoolboy can be top of the class—while his father supports him at school. You may be a great intellectual and still psycho-sexually inadequate, still reluctant to shoulder the responsibilities of the prime minister in your dream. Or, in a general sense, still not happy in the role of absolute monarch, not quite fitting as leader in all spheres, philosophic, economic, social and sexual. Are you going to attain leadership in one of these at the expense of one or more of the others?

"It is possible that none of us really dares psychologically to seize leadership. Even the Archbishop of Canterbury gains his strength from a greater Almighty Father-figure, and Hitler from an ideal (however satanic) which he feels to be greater than himself.

"Looking at the matter in this light it seems that no person is able utterly and consistently to usurp the place of his father *in toto*. He can only succeed in doing so to a limited extent with the proviso that he sets up an alternative father to support him and give courage to his daring.

"After all, none of us is really the Almighty, none of us was responsible for his own creation, none of us has power over his own individual destiny. Each of us is a victim of nature's realities, to no less an extent than he is the victim of his own delusions. We begin life as the son, and whatever limited father usurpations we may achieve we nevertheless continue and end our lives still the son."

In spite of these rather unanalytical soliloquies, the purpose of which on my part had been to wind up the patient's tendency to philosophize by some degree of reassurance that I would not interfere with his beliefs and so enable him to continue analysis, he was not completely satisfied.

At the next session he re-opened the subject: "I have got yesterday's problem in a nutshell. Do you permit in a completely analysed patient a residuum of religion, or is evidence of religious belief only just another symptom? If it is then we are going to be at loggerheads. You must not take away my religion. Declare yourself for or against.

"What is the completely analysed person like? Won't he always be a nonentity, satisfied completely, as a result of his analysis, in the gratification of his instincts? Have any analysed persons become great? Is not greatness an abnormality, the symptom of repressed instincts? The choice is between happy animal life, life of the ordinary person, or id repression and consequent ego greatness, which is it to be?"

Analyst: "Which would you rather have?"

Patient: "That is a difficult question to answer. You have me either way. If I say I would rather have ego greatness you will tell me that that is my ego talking and my id would rather have something different, but you won't tell me what my id wants. You will call the whole of this session an 'ego-herring,' but you refuse to come into the open.

"I know that you often analyse impotent men and you expect them to go away with a normal erection. Now I hold that it is just as 'natural' for a patient to go away with a religious belief."

Analyst: "What is a man's religion?"

Patient: "It is a man's conscious recognition of a deity and his ability to communicate with Him through prayer."

After a few moments' silence this exceptionally intelligent patient said: "I fully appreciate that all this discussion can be interpreted as a struggle or fight between us in which each may be represented as trying to castrate the other. My position is that I am afraid that you are going to cut off a part of me, perhaps my most valuable part."

Analyst: "Which end are you referring to?"

Patient: "They are the same, and now I will give you a word for it. I will call it my 'ego-erection.'

"There is very little difference between an intellectual fight and a physical one. In each case one party is trying to cut off something of the other party's, whether this is opinion or belief on the one hand and his head or his sex on the other.

"Is there any difference between the ego-erection of ideas, derived from the id's energy, and the ordinary id erection or phallus? Each party is trying to be in the dominant role, and put it across the other party, cut off his ideas and put in one's own, or I suppose cut off the other's masculinity and impregnate him with one's own personality.

"So I come to the conclusion that there is very little essential difference between an intellectual argument, a fight, and a sexual struggle. But you see my Free Association of Thought has as usual led me right away from the real ego point. The real question is what is the object of analysis? Is it going to take away my religious beliefs? If so, I'm off now."

Analyst: "Perhaps you deserve some sort of an answer on the conscious plane since you have already interpreted something of the source of your anxiety and, partly at least, recognized its early roots in the original Oedipus struggle.

"The purpose of analysis is not to take anything away

from the patient, least of all his religion. It would be as unjustifiable to attempt this as to attempt to take away his sexual potency. Admittedly, this last attempt has been made throughout our lives by parent-figures and mentors, that is why as you point out we get so many patients here requiring its restoration. Analysis must not take away anything valuable to the patient's psyche, whether that valuable be id potency or 'ego-erection.' Its purpose is to show the patient the unconscious causes behind his actions, desires and thoughts.

"This session may be interpreted as having its source in the original struggle between the boy and his father. In your unconscious emotional life you felt that father was the more potent and would therefore prevent you from achieving potency or deprive you of any potency which you had already achieved.

"You were very frightened. The question was whether to run away for safety or to stand and fight him. Well, you have stood, or rather lain, and fought him! And if as a result you feel reassured that potency, be it translated into any form of 'ego-erection,' will not be taken from you and you are safe to go on lying here and being yourself, we may presently in the absence of further anxiety, progress to the next stage of your analysis."

There are several drives at work within the patient. One which has come out in these last two sessions shows the normal tendency to fight the father in order to attain, or to preserve, psycho-sexual manhood oneself. The *form* which this tendency takes is relatively unimportant. It so happens that in this patient and at this point it took the form of a tendency to argument.

But it is of some secondary interest that the subject chosen for the argument was religious belief because this suggests that though the analyst was being fought off as though he were a father-image, still a father-image was being cherished and clung to (religious belief) in the role of the saviour or preserver.

Thus the unconscious ambivalence (the primitive pattern of love and hate for the same person, or image, at the same time) of fixation to the father is revealed, albeit the original single object is here split into two objects, God and analyst.

So the material here reveals to us two drives, one to cling to the father for added potency and two to fight off a bad father image which is phantasied as determined to destroy that potency. Nevertheless, in both instances the emotional concern is with the *father*-image. No heterosexual tendency has yet revealed itself.

With the lessening of the patient's anxiety he ceases to fight the analyst as the bad father-image but tends rather to accept him as the good father-image.

With this acceptance his libido, aim-inhibited and sex-repressed in regard to his religious emotional life, reveals itself unmistakably at his subsequent sessions in his positive attitude to the analyst. Some aspects of the difficulties which ensue will be shown in the next chapter.

Chapter VIII

The Homosexual Component and the Defences Against it—With the Hint of a Deeper Heterosexual Level

IN THE last chapter we saw how the patient's positive transference to the father-image presently led him to an exposition of his positive transference to the Almighty Father, to his religion, and how at the same time his *negative* transference to the father image gave rise to the fear that his earthly "father" (in the form of his analyst) would deprive him, perhaps through jealousy, of what he held to be of the highest value—namely his religion.

Now presently it came to be revealed that with the reduction of his anxiety on this latter score the repressed homosexual component of his original father worship underwent increasing unrepression so that in the absence of anxiety we gradually reached the position in which the patient was playing with phantasies of actual physical intimacy with the father-image in the shape of his analyst.

Beginning with the memories of the joy he had as a small boy of getting into bed with his daddy he took to eyeing me with an increasing interest, and it was not long before he was tentatively speculating upon the idea of what it would feel like to get closer to me.

He said: "There is a special pleasure in being close to someone you like. What excitement I used to have in getting into bed with my father! What a funny, but rather thrilling idea it would be to get into bed with you!"

Analyst: "Suppose you pursue that phantasy."

Patient: "My feeling is that it would lead up to something exciting. I can't get away from the feeling that it would be very gratifying. I admit that I feel very embarrassed about it, but whether I think of getting into bed with you or with father it would be embarrassing both ways. I think it is embarrassing because it means so much. It is pregnant with so much possibility. A man like my father would be such an exciting thing to be in bed with. At the same time I feel I cannot bear the idea."

Analyst: "The embarrassment is an attribute of the ego, do you think, due to acquired ideas rather than to instincts?"

Patient: "Yes, I think it is just fear of the enormous possibilities. You see, he's got to love you more and more. I am inclined to say you are forcing me into this position though I admit it's a position which I could not resist. I feel that if I could not be blamed in any way I would enjoy it. It would be a kind of surrender. I want a leader in every respect, somebody to take the blame away from me so that I could surrender to him.

"I had a dream the other night that I was sitting on the front of a train, right in front of the engine, and all the train was behind me, in fact I couldn't see the train at all, only the railway track in front of me as I was, as it were, pushed along by the train.

"There was a lot more in it which I cannot remember, but I can tell you this much: the train was on its way to Yarmouth and that was the journey that I did with my daddy when I was between the age of two and a half and three. I was sitting on his knee with my legs either side of his knee and leaning forward in exactly the same position as I was on the front of this engine in the dream. I was having a thoroughly happy time, thoroughly enjoying myself. The feeling is one of enormous security and of immense power.

"Perhaps that's what people mean when they say they have their father "behind them," and that's the sense of power that one gets with the religious feeling of being in the right, of having God behind one.

"Incidentally, it reminds me of how I loved to play with railway engines. They, too, gave me this sense of power in a minor way, and I might as well admit right now that engines have never lost their fascination for me.

The bigger and stronger they are the more they thrill me. I know that it is the same with many men. Grown up boys, that's what we all are."

Then followed Associations of Thought to the significance of himself sitting on the foremost part of the train with a powerful engine behind and under his seat pushing him forcefully along and the sense of enormous power and satisfaction that he gained from it. Before long he identified this train and engine with a sense of father's potency, and concluded that it represented the all powerful phallus and was astounded to discover that he had an ungratified and previously unsuspected homosexual element in his unconscious emotional make-up. Further, he discovered that it was this element which had supplied the overwhelming force of his father-attachment and which was now the power behind his transference attachment to his analyst.

We have only lately left the very thorny subject of religion to find ourselves embarked upon an even thornier subject. One should reflect that it is the work of deep mental analysis to arouse every thorny subject, everything about which we are particularly touchy, about which we preserve a conspiracy of silence.

The fact is that analysis has to do with the unconscious —and it is unconscious because of resistance. It has been repressed from consciousness because we were too touchy to endure it, to tolerate it. Analysis enables the unconscious to become conscious by weakening and removing resistance.

The difficulty about writing case-material for those who are not psycho-analysts is that the subject matter that is really deep enough to be therapeutically effective is too thorny, too strongly, even too violently and desperately repressed to be acceptable or tolerable to the normal mind of the average reader without a graduated process of unrepression.

In fact, the effectiveness of mental constellations in

producing disease is directly in proportion to the forcefulness with which they are repressed. That is why the writer is handicapped in a way that would not be the case with a patient. In the case of a patient he can wait, he can bide his time for a very gradual diminution of repressive forces by graduated stages.

No patient or reader is benefited by premature interpretation, that is to say by interpretations that do not take into account the repressions and biases upon which the reader's character has been built and which at the same time are responsible for what might be called character-armour in the normal, and symptoms in the case of the so-called ill.

So it would seem to the analyst that we are all in a sense ill people, mentally ill by virtue of our limitations if not actually the victims of symptoms. The writer has to beware of everybody's mental corns. The writer has to sacrifice forcefulness and explicitness to the policy of treading lightly on account of these corns.

However, we may permit ourselves to return to the patient for a few moments just to catch him up at the stage of analysis where he finds his homosexual phantasies running so gravely counter to reality that he realizes there is no possible fulfilment of them in a real world. Then reaction-formation sets in and he says:

"According to my standards I think it is all horrible. These feelings were meant for heterosexual purposes, and here I find that my feelings, *mine*, have all got tangled up with father. It is father, father, father all my life. Interested in him mentally, interested in him physically; it is only him or his successors that I am interested in. And here I have been trying to force myself to take an interest in women. I can see now how ridiculous it is."

An interesting fact is that throughout this time that the patient's emotional life was completely wrapped up with father-images, his attitude towards women was not so much one of emotional disinterest as one of ego-disparagement. He refers contemptuously to them: "Those creatures with their curiously shaped bodies, comical I call it, and with their hair and their paint and their funny, illogical ideas, patting their hair! How on earth could anybody with any sense fall in love with a thing like that!"

I reminded him that it was not very long ago (particularly during a part of the analysis when he had a very strong transference to me) that he was having many and varied relations with women.

His reply to this was significant.

He said: "I was acting the part of daddy. Daddy would play with mummy, and I would play with girls. But the whole point about it was that I could come back and tell *you* all about it. Now that I am beginning to find that you are not daddy after all, there is no point in telling you all about it and therefore no point in doing it.

"Now I have got nothing at all. There is nothing worth doing. Women are silly sort of things. I don't think I want to have anything to do with them at all. The tragedy of it is that I am also losing interest in analysis. I want you to tell me what I am to do with any women I meet at the party tonight."

Analyst: "You've lost your daddy and you haven't yet found any woman."

Patient: "Of course I have lost my daddy, that ideal love. It made it quite impossible for me to accept any reality loving, therefore I thought if I couldn't get the thing absolutely right, it's not worth bothering about. It was all very well to have the daddy-response always available, as it were, between my legs whenever I wanted it, the perfect portable loving machine (pocket model!), but when I want to bring my love into relationship with reality what's the good of that; it's only a handicap, an intolerable handicap. I am much better without it, without this wretched phantasy of bliss with a dead father.

"If my mind does tend to make it real, as I have seen it does, what does it lead to then? To homosexuality. If

my instinct does want that, *I* do not. For one thing I can
see that that sort of love also is impossible to bring into
a satisfactory relationship with reality. So there again we
see how it is. My emotional life is something quite apart
from reality, from real living at all. I am thrown back
into this position of dissociation from real life, from real
people. There seems to be no contact for me."

As was to be expected, the patient was in for a period
of depression. He arrived at his next session to face the complete emptiness of life. This was interpretable as: "No
father, no mother, nothing at all."

He said: "I have spent the week-end at home in bed
sleeping, or attempting to sleep. I have never felt so
depressed in my life as I did on Sunday. Now I come to
think of it this day was just an epitome of what my life
has been throughout, of what led me to come to analysis
for help.

"I can see what I have been doing. I have been building
up a lot of ego-activity to use up the time. It was really
all a defence against the danger of falling back upon my
own thoughts, upon my own emotional emptiness, or
rather the emptiness or non-existence of my emotional
relationship to reality and to other people. So far analysis
seems to have removed or exposed the falsity of my ego-
constructions. It has given me little or nothing in place
of them.

"Strangely enough over the week-end my sleeping life
has not been so empty as my waking life. The former has
at least been full of dreams in which I have been particularly active. The latter has been just emptiness, with
a few masturbatory acts thrown in.

"I remember only two fragments of dreams. They were
on the same night. In the first I was a prisoner at German
headquarters. There were lots of motor cars and helmets
with spikes on them, proper masculine phallic things all
around. I escaped.

"In the second dream I was with a lovely woman and

we went to a public house for a drink or a meal. That's all I can remember about it."

These two little fragments speak more to the analyst than anything the patient could say on the conscious plane with the usual dissemblings of the ego. They tell the analyst that *deep down* he is anxious to escape from the father, the male image, and to find happiness or satisfaction with the female. In short, they are normal Oedipus dreams of getting rid of father and achieving mother, or, we might say, of repudiating homosexuality. To dream this has a very different significance from expressing it as an ego idea.

In his sleep he solved the problem, but in his waking life he has resisted its solution. Therefore his waking hours are spent with a sense of frustration and depression such as he suffered during the week-end.

At this very session he confirms our interpretation by the following rationalized though lucid statement:

"I know that what I am fighting against is the ability to make loving a conscious act. I know that I am resisting it. It is easy for me to resist it. I have done so all my life. It is more than a habit. I resist it unconsciously.

"I know also why I resist it. It is because I do not want to be dependent on somebody else. I refuse absolutely to surrender my liberty and independence, my very soul, to anybody on this earth. I cannot see myself ever surrendering. I believe that I shall always refuse."

While this patient on a conscious plane was almost exclusively preoccupied with males and more specifically with experiencing a very positive relationship towards his analyst, he was at the same time denying and repudiating any sort of emotional affect towards the female, except occasionally when she seemed to thrust herself upon him and then his affect would be of a predominantly negative nature. There seems to be a relationship between his positive attitude towards males, originally the father, and his corresponding negative attitude towards the female, originally his mother. But, while this was the conscious aspect of his mentality, at the same time his dreams, or some of them, seemed to belie it. These latter seemed to indicate a search not so much for the male, but actually for the female which he was consciously repudiating. What is more, the dream material pointed very often to that particular female, the first in his emotional experience, namely, to his mother, a person who consciously occupied him least of all, unless it was negatively when she dared to thrust her presence upon him. However, the analyst grows accustomed to believe dreams rather than the dissembling ego, the conscious-level talk. Here is an example of what I mean.

He said: "I dreamt last night that I was back at the firm that I used to work for before the war in Liverpool where I lived with my mother. I felt a little strange working there. The time came for lunch, the recreation interval. All my workmates went off together and I go out by myself into the town to find a place for lunch. I walk up and down the town without finding a place. I go up on to some high ground on the outskirts of the town and then return again to the town. While returning I notice two or three boys on the edge of a cliff trying to push each other over the edge. Back in the town I find an hotel and ask diffidently if they can give me lunch. To my surprise it seems possible that they can. So I go out again to bring my car up to the hotel. It is dark outside, and I am anxious as to whether I will find the place where I left the car. After a long search in the dark at length I find the place, and, this is the remarkable thing, *my mother is there*. She and I get into the car and I start driving it. Then we run out of petrol. I pour some more into the tank. That's the end of the dream."

Analyst: "What do you think of it?"

Patient: "Well to me the amazing thing is that it ends up, after my search, by my finding myself with my mother in the car—my mother, the last person I want to be with. It is lunch I am searching for, and then the car. Lunch is gratification—I know what the car is: a phallic symbol. The amazing thing is that it should be back with my mother—Good Lord!"

The patient has practically interpreted the essential elements of the dream. It speaks volumes, much more than his conscious mind would ever speak or even believe —at least at the present stage of his analysis. It seems that that is why he is lost, wandering about in the town and out of the town, about life, not finding any lunch, not finding any gratification, not finding any woman. It is because he is refusing to go back to where it all lies, namely, where mother is. But what do we find when the patient has interpreted the essence of his dream? Instead of accepting it he goes on to say:

"I hate the idea of liking my mother. To me it is repulsive."

Analyst: "Why?"

Patient: "Because it is not an equal love, not a love between two mature adults. It is a love between excessive maturity on the one hand and immaturity on the other. It's a silly sort of love to have, it's unbalanced. I hate the idea of it, it revolts me . . . to like one's mother . . . ugh! I can't escape the loathing I have to any sort of emotional relationship to my mother. Is it that I am doing all that I can to suppress the emotion for my mother?"

Analyst: "What is your Free Association of Thought to this feeling of repugnance?"

Patient: "Being sloppy and soft and wet."

Analyst: "Free Association to that."

Patient: "Oh, things like nappies and breasts, essentially female. They are all sloppy and wet. It's just like women to be wet—inside and out. It reminds me of an awful little bitch I met once—it makes me almost sick to think of her—and then to think of mother . . . wet . . . wet . . . wet . . . wet!"

Later it will be seen that these apparent or conscious causes of his revulsion for women are typical rationalizations. As I hinted before the real causes will be seen to

have their source in classical castration phantasies—
totally unconscious and illogical. The time was not yet
ripe for an interpretation of these.

Analyst: "It seems that as long as you have this repugnance for mother you have it for all women. Apparently
they are all similarly wet."

Patient: "Oh yes, I sée it. I am revolted. Mother is
a nuisance in every respect. Mother wants a daughter
now. And I am the only means of her getting a daughter.
She could only get a daughter by my 'adopting' one for
her, by my marrying a wife. I feel somehow that mother
has got me below the belt . . . got me where I can't
retaliate. She's wet, and prudish—what an awful com-
bination! A man is stiff and hard and dry—give me a man
every time . . . no sloppiness and no prudishness either,
whereas in a woman you have both."

Analyst: "Can it be that you are really attracted to this
wetness, but when you go to approach it you are met by
mother's prudishness? Is it something like putting sugar
on a dog's nose and tormenting it?"

Patient: "Do you mean to say I really want to have
wetness? I find that hard to believe. I can only think of
it all as revolting."

Analyst: "Well, perhaps there was a time in your life
when you liked wetness; as a baby you certainly liked a
wet breast. Might it be that this revulsion has only come
as a reaction-formation, perhaps as a result of your being
repulsed, of your not being able to indulge freely in wetness? For instance, if you put sweets in front of a dog and
whip it every time it goes for it the dog eventually learns
to hate sweets."

Patient: "Oh yes, and I suppose my position is that I
don't know whether to hate the whip or the sweets."

Analyst: "So you have buried the attraction of mother,
repressed that, but when you go to look for your car, the
car which will take you to the lunch, to gratification,
you find mother there."

Patient: "Now I come to think of it in the dream it

was a particularly dirty little car, and that reminds me mother always used to call my organ 'All dirty.' That was her name for it. It was always referred to by that name and by nothing else . . . 'all dirty.' It is amazing that my unconscious should bring this out. And there in the dream I am wandering about not knowing where to get lunch, just like I wander about through life not knowing how to enjoy it, how to get any pleasure out of it, and when I am getting hot, that is to say getting near the lunch, near the gratification, lo and behold I find mother there! Mother and the dirty little car seem to go together. It gives me some food for thought. Though I confess it's beyond me."

At a later stage we will see that the "reasons" this patient gives for his resistance to heterosexual love are merely rationalizations. The real "reason" emerges later in connection with a dream. It proves to be not so reasonable. It is nothing less than this: He believes that every woman starting with his mother has a horrible "crocodile" inside her body which will maim, mutilate or devour him if he should enter. Naturally he is at present unconscious of the text of this belief, though only too conscious of its affect—of its emotional content—which latter is effective in controlling his reactions and behaviours.

What a reflection on the human psyche that it should be the subject, the victim, of such absurd infantile phantasies! That it is even normally in the throes of such absurdities is only too well evidenced by its institutionalization and expression of them, past, present—and future. The inquisitions, past and present, the witch-burnings of the Middle Ages, superstitions and beliefs, irrationality and "rationality," laws and wars, all bear witness.

In the narrower field of individual psychology our patient is no exception to the general rule of irrational biases and preferences. Fetishes are as absurd as revulsions.

For instance, we may see this clearly in the case of the homosexual patient with a preference for boys of fourteen

G

who raved to me about the "wonderful knees" of a particular youth, yet miss it in the case of the poet who writes "odes to his mistress's eyebrow," or in the case of the man who married a girl on account of her marvellous blonde hair.

The preference for the fetish is based on a no less incredible, unconscious phantasy than the revulsion of the "crocodile" in the case of our patient.

But we shall return to this later.

BOOK TWO

MOTHER

Chapter IX

The Emergence of the Mother-Fixation
from Beneath the Father-Fixation

BEARING IN MIND that this patient's cardinal sympton
was his vehemently avowed distaste for women, it may
surprise us to hear from him another fairly typical dream
in which the outstanding feature is the exact opposite of
what he consciously avows, namely a dream revealing a
strong mental and physical attraction towards what he
calls a particularly charming member of the opposite sex.

Until an advanced stage of his analysis, they had never
succeeded in charming him on a conscious plane, that is
to say during his waking conscious life, but in his sleep it
is apparently a different story. He brings me this dream:

"The scene was a wood. We were there for a kind of
picnic. There were three people sitting on the ground; one
was a woman. She beckoned me to sit beside her, which I
did. She was very friendly and nice.

"Then the scene changed to that of a schoolroom, and
we were still sitting together. She became amorous, holding my hand and trying to kiss me. I liked her very much.
She was a most charming person. The lecturer in the
classroom wasn't very good and he didn't pay much
attention to what we were doing in the schoolroom. She
grew more and more amorous, I mean erotically inclined,
so I pushed her violently away and tried to pretend I was
having nothing to do with her. I did this because I
couldn't bear the possibility of the lecturer seeing this
amorous performance.

"This was followed by another dream, in which I asked
an old friend of mine and his wife how the trial was
getting on. They said they didn't let this subject enter
their minds. That was all."

Leaving aside for the moment the more important

transference aspects of the first dream ("the 'lecturer' wasn't very good, etc,") fully realizing that these will have to be dealt with at the first opportunity, this dream brought to our notice something which might otherwise have escaped us. It was this:

Throughout this patient's life in his relationship to women it has always been the woman who took the initiative. We noticed in the dream it was she that beckoned him, it was she who was friendly and nice, it was she who made all the advances. The patient admits that it is always thus. Never once in his whole existence has he made the first advance to a woman.

More than this, occasions have arisen when he has been particularly intimate with a woman at her initiative, and yet when he sees this woman even a day or two later he makes no advance whatsoever. Until she again takes the initiative he may in her presence be feeling embarrassment at the thought of her making some suggestion to him, though this embarrassment may disappear if she does make advances.

He excuses himself by saying "How could I take the initiative and make a fuss of her when for all I know within a day or two I might not feel at all affectionate 'owards her? That would place me in a very awkward position."

Again, he says, he feels embarrassed until she makes a second or third advance because, he says, he wouldn't be sure of himself. He wouldn't be sure of his response; it might not be what was expected of him. "I always need encouragement from a woman, a lot of encouragement. If the woman is indifferent, I am indifferent. I respond only to her encouragement."

Analyst: "Does nothing arise from within yourself? Do you yourself never get any feeling towards a woman until she has shown that she desires you?"

Patient: "No, there is no guide at all. And if there were and I were to show the slightest sign of it . . . I couldn't, I couldn't show any sign, because I would be terrified of deceiving her by it. Also I assume that she would resent any advance from me. So much is this the case that I am afraid to let any feelings arise from within me. Always it is I who have been seduced by women, never the other way round. Perhaps that is why I say I do not want a woman. I really feel I do not need it, I can always fall back upon myself."

At the next session the patient continued with this subject.

He said: "I have been thinking of what is apparently your definition of a normal man's nature: that he should get spontaneous desires towards a woman without her having previously encouraged him. It seems to me extraordinary to set out to dominate a female. The thought in my mind is: 'Well, if you do that you've done it! What will you do after you have done all your dominating? You may not want her anyhow.' "

Analyst: "Apparently somebody's got to make the first move. In your case it is always the woman. She is doing the very thing that you regard as so amazing in a man, namely, responding to some desire from within her. The only suggestion I made is that it is even more usual for a man to take the initiative and cause the woman to respond to some desire that arises from within him."

Patient: "Well, I can see that intellectually, but I cannot think it."

Analyst: "Do you never see a girl that attracts you so that you desire her?"

Patient: "No, I don't think so. Well, let me see . . . sometimes I'm sort of superficially attracted to a pretty face or something."

Analyst: "Well, if you are attracted what does that mean? Doesn't that mean that you want to go nearer to that pretty face? Perhaps to get to know it, perhaps to do something to it, or even possibly to possess it, to feel that it is yours."

"Oh, no," the patient laughs, "If I am attracted by a person or a face it never occurs to me to make any advance

or to feel that I ought to possess her. I am thinking that I
have been told too often by my parents what I ought to
like, that's why I don't know what I do like—if anything.

"The same applies to everything in my life. If I see a
car that I like it never occurs to me to try to possess it. I
would only possess a car for utilitarian purposes. The
same applies to clothes; usually there I don't know even
what to like. If I do like any particular kind of clothes it
never occurs to me to adopt it and make it mine. Food
also, there may be certain foods that I like, but it never
occurs to me to order those foods. I order food merely
from the point of view of value. Apparantly I put aside all
my likes, if I have any likes. The same applies to every
single thing I can think of in life.

"But I realize this, all these matters are only *secondary*
. . . they are all secondary to my main inability, namely,
that I don't know how to like a woman.

"If I knew how to like a woman, then I would have
some initiative in all my other likes and dislikes. I
would behave differently to cars, to books, to clothes,
to everything in life, in fact to life itself. I can see that
the whole problem radiates from this inability to get
a spontaneous desire of liking and so on towards a
woman."

Analyst: "The metaphor that occurs to me is that of a
jewel enthusiast who was once a jewel thief, who now dare
not like any jewellery because he has been so thoroughly
warned off it, so frightened to like, or, if some liking does
creep in, even more terrified to take any notice of it. As
though the danger were too great. Isn't that it?"

Patient: "Yes, it may be, it does feel like that. But what
can one do about it all anyway? Let us have a long chat
about it."

Analyst: "No! We have spent long enough discussing
it. It is time you told me the dreams you had last night."

Patient: "Oh, hang the dreams! You've had enough of
those."

Analyst: "The only valuable contribution to this problem will come to you from your unconscious and your dreams will open the door to that."

It was because the patient at this session was bent upon evading analysis in favour of conscious intellectual discussion that I considered it necessary to adopt this most unusual analytical procedure of insisting that he related the dreams of the previo s night in spite of his resistance and his consequent ego conviction that they were a waste of time.

I would like to stress that while conscious-level discussion goes round and round making a few tentative suggestions but never getting to anything really convincing, the dreams on the contrary with one swift stroke bring the matter, the hidden matter in which lies the solution to the whole problem, straight before us.

Dream material is "straight from the horse's mouth." Of course it is necessary to learn to understand the language of the "horse," but having understood it we have something which Nature says, something which is the truth itself, in contradistinction to the dissembling of the ego.

The patient said: "Oh, well, then, here are the dreams. There were three tiny ones and a fourth slightly longer. Of course they mean nothing.

"The first dream: I am in a lift going up and down fast. Two men I know are with me. One is an elderly man whom we called 'Father Tom' and the other is a young man whose name is Thompson.

"In the second dream I am in my flat with two other men. It's a sort of men's party.

"In the third dream I am learning to ride a motor-bike. I am sitting on it and Father Tom is teaching me.

"The fourth, and longer dream, is a more curious bit of nonsense. It's about an underground cavern in America, and this underground cavern is half full of water. Some American soldiers went into it and some of them got maimed, partly eaten up, by an enormous giant crocodile that lived in the water.

"In the dream I seemed to be looking at photographs in an illustrated paper of the cavern and the crocodile and the men. Shall we take the dreams in order?"

Analyst: "All right, what is the Free Association of Thought to this going up and down fast in a lift?"

"A curious thought comes to me that during sexual excitement my feeling periodically disappears. It's just the *feeling* that disappears, it seems to go down and disappear altogether and then come up again. It can do that fast in rapid succession.

"The two people with me in the lift . . . of course, one is obviously a father-figure, in fact we call him 'father' and the other I suppose is his son, which must be me. Odd, isn't it? I thought I had done with all that homosexual nonsense with father.

"Perhaps the reason my feelings go suddenly is because I am liking father instead of a woman. That's why it goes up and down. You can't keep up a continuous sexual feeling in relation to a male. I suppose there is too much conflict or something about it, it comes and goes, or goes and comes.

"There was also a little anxiety in that dream that the lift might crash at any moment. I can see that the second dream is something of the same sort. Again it is an attempted homosexual solution, again not very satisfactory.

"In the third dream I have got this complicated, powerful machine between my legs learning to use it as I am learning in this room. I suppose you are the father-figure in this instance.

"And then in the fourth dream at last we get the feminine symbol. This blessed underground cavern, half filled with water too, wet as any woman ready for phallic symbols, the sort of mutts who go in and get eaten up or maimed in some way or other!

"The crocodile was the deuce of a fellow, sixty feet

long . . . sixty . . . why that's the age my father would be if he were still alive. But I can't imagine this crocodile as father . . . unless he was a sort of bogey-man father . . . an enemy father, like the spiked German helmets in the other dream . . . horrible.

"Yes, I can see that if there's a kind of crocodile inside every woman, there is also the feeling that one might get eaten up if one went inside . . . trapped and caught. I must see to it that I am not as vulnerable as all that. Of course, I can see it now.

"One would certainly hesitate to go into a woman if there were a crocodile inside. You remember I confessed that if there were a dozen women lined up, I might find one or two more attractive than the others, but what I stressed was this, that however attractive the one or two might be it would in a sense leave me cold. I would make no advance. I would never take an attractive girl and pet her, or anything like that.

"No, I would make not one single step forward. My feeling is as though they are not for use, not for me . . . and I can quite see that, if there is a sixty-foot crocodile in them.

"What does it matter, then, if one is a bit more attractive than another? The main point is the crocodile, not the attractiveness of the cavern or its environs. I don't care if it's made of ivory or precious stones, if I know there's a crocodile behind each of those doors you can keep your ivory and your precious stones. I'm off.

"The only thing that makes the slightest difference in the situation is if the woman says 'Come in. There's no crocodile in my house.' But even then I hesitate. I don't know whether I'll be any good to her, for how can you be sure?

"In any case you couldn't see the crocodile inside her, and every woman has a crocodile of some sort. If she's married she has a husband, if she's single she has parents; they'll all be after you. If she's a widow she will trap you anyhow.

"Only if you drink enough, and it's only when I have drunk that I've ever done anything with a woman, it's only if you drink enough that you can get brave enough —have enough Dutch courage to brave all the crocodiles. Then you can say to yourself 'What's a crocodile anyway!' You don't care if you die. Over the top after your rum ration, into the cannon's mouth!"

Before long the patient was back in infantile phantasies which were related to the above material.

He said: "When baby is put into a cot by mother, then father comes and takes away the mother. That's awful for the baby. It isn't as though they were going off to see some other baby, that wouldn't be so bad, but mother is actually being taken away by this man for him to use for his purposes. Once out of it the man is in it, and it seems to me that he must be inside for evermore, and there's no room for me.

"These attractive women! Somehow or other, although I say they are attractive, they do not attract me, not in the way they appear to attract other men. And as for mother herself . . . oh well, that's the original danger. I give that a wide berth evidently. I can only see the water or wetness and feel there's something repulsive, horrid; perhaps it isn't the wetness. I don't know what it is. It's that wretched crocodile inside!"

Material gained in this way from dreams, although most interesting and illuminating to the psychologist, has unfortunately, at least at the time when it first emerges, practically no therapeutic effect upon the patient. It is straight from the horse's mouth all right, and in a sense the patient may have learned the horse's language, but the bridge between this unconscious-level horse and his thinking mind, his ego, is not complete. Perhaps there is practically no bridge at all, something has just jumped across the gulf, or something jumps backwards and forwards, but no permanent connection has been established, no therapeutic effect is as yet available.

Nevertheless, the analyst, and in some instances (though these are rare) the patient, may realize that what previously seemed an insoluble riddle now gives at least an inkling that it is not insoluble at all.

As a matter of fact, we have the solution before us. The answer has been given even if we hear it only dimly and as if from afar. In many, perhaps in the majority of cases of psycho-sexual impotence, the phantasy responsible for the man's total impotence is none other than this phantasy which this patient, though not himself totally impotent, has here revealed to us; the classical phantasy of the father's phallus within the mother's body—the phallus that has sharp teeth, thus showing its primitive origin from the oral-sadistic, biting stage of libidinal development.

In the last chapter it was stated that the "reasons" which the patient gave for his distaste of women were no more than rationalizations, consciously adduced "explanations" for feelings which had their real source in unconscious and illogical formulations; formulations which would have been totally unacceptable to his ego had they been presented to consciousness.

It was promised that the source of his hatred or revulsion would be subsequently revealed. And now, he himself has revealed it to us as an unconscious phantasy, having its inception in earliest infancy (if not hereditarily), of the preposterous conviction that within the woman's body (originally mother's) there lurks a most horrible monster, a monster endowed with all the savage aggression of the biting stage of libidinal (and racial) development.

The psyche has at some early level projected its primitive oral lusts and created out of them this demon which subsequently becomes identified with the persons and part-objects that frustrate and "castrate" its later desires.

The practical point is that such phantasies, however ridiculous to the adult ego, are affectively charged;

indeed from them can emanate almost the whole of the affective charge applied to a present-day situation, so that they are emotionally effective in influencing, even controlling, not only our feelings, our physiological and psychological responses, but even, unwittingly, our judgments and reason itself.

Truths, or rather the untruths, upon which our reactions, including those of our reason itself, are built, prove indeed far stranger than anything fiction would dare to present.

Chapter X

Father Gives Place to Mother

THE CROCODILE dream appeared to have more effect upon this patient than had been anticipated at the time. He arrived at his next session in a happy, elated mood. He thought his improved condition was entirely due to the exposure of the crocodile dream and the picture of his infancy that followed it.

He said: "Regarding that picture of the infant in its cradle and the idea of my losing my mother to my father: father could only be so horrible as the crocodile when he was approaching the mother that I wanted. It could only happen if you saw them together, if you saw the father taking the mother away, and it would have to be played out in front of the infant. It makes me think 'no wonder I could never like my mother because there was the crocodile always near at hand.' What is of interest in that picture is that it is created entirely by myself. She cuddles me and puts me into the cot and father comes in and what does he do? He steals my mother and I am left to cry my heart out in the cot. I remember now that mother has told me that my father used to say 'Don't go up to him, you'll spoil him. Just let him cry.' Obviously one could have no feelings or likings if one's central desire at such an early age, as a mere baby in a cot, was left ungratified."

This patient seems very sure that the policy of avoiding the "spoiling" of a baby by leaving it to cry itself out in a cot, a policy of which he was the victim, was the first, the most serious and traumatic, cause of the dislocation of his emotional pattern.

He says: "Obviously one could have no feelings or likings if that, one's central desire (for the mother), was left ungratified at such an early age. Something has to die. The baby may not die, not physically, but in some psycho-

logical way, some emotional way, death takes place. My
body has grown since, but you and I both know very well
that there is *something dead in me*" (vide Chapter XI).

Fathers who unconsciously wish to destroy their
babies would naturally support this policy on the rationalized grounds of proper upbringing, of avoiding spoiling.
But I fancy that the good mother's natural instinct would
not be to leave a baby to cry itself out. Love preserves life
and health; discipline or training, which is often merely
rationalized hate, if it does not destroy them, commonly
distorts their shape to fit the mould of an already mis-
shapen culture. *And this is the aetiology of all human ills and
illness.*

The patient continued: "The tragedy in my case was
that that feeling would not get any natural correction as
it would do in the case of one who was not an only child.
Of course it was my phantasy and not my parents' behaviour that made me so stupid about it all, and there
were no other children that followed to break up my
phantasy. Other children following me would have
shown me that something less powerful than me had a
claim on sharing the mother, and one would begin at the
age of say eighteen months to understand tolerance. In
my case that absurd phantasy was never modified."

An interesting reflection on at least one possible cause
of the commonly observed clinical phenomenon that a
large proportion of psycho-neurotics are only children!

"I never found that my mother was being stolen by
another infant. It was always a most powerful person.
How impossible for an infant to pit its tiny potency, its
tiny claim on the mother, against the father, because the
father would win all the time. The only way is to be
attractive to father, and you do this not merely to placate
an enemy, but in order to keep an interest in him or
rather to keep him interested in you; that is to say if you
attract father he will stay and so keep mother by the cot-
side. If you present a small person with a person who
would be an impossibly powerful enemy, what can he do

except make friends with him? As I have said, it was all my stupid phantasy and nothing to do with my parents' behaviour, but I am happier today because I appreciate that this concept explains a great deal to me. It explains this disinclination to like anybody, this absence of feeling, because it only becomes unbearably awful to like the mother when the father is so powerful. Therefore the only way out is to sit on the whole lot, to crush all one's feelings. I always say I don't know what I would like to do, because if the thing you like to do *best* is repressed, then you don't know any of the secondaries."

Analyst: "What is the thing you like to do best?"

Patient: "Well, at that age it was to grab mother, to have mother, to enjoy mother without interruption, without father. Of course, I know you won't believe in all this, although if it was in my dreams you would believe it."

Analyst: "Let us have your dreams."

Patient: "Now I come to think of it, it was mother I was dreaming about. I dreamt I was in a bedroom putting my mother to bed and saying good-night to her. It is only early evening, still daylight, but she, poor thing, must go to bed early at 6.15 while I go on to a party. The party takes place in a power-house and no one is allowed to start up the machinery until 4 o'clock. But at five minutes to four somebody starts some of the machinery working. President Roosevelt then comes in and together we examine a new type of instrument which compensates the variations of movement of a needle point. (End of dream.)"

In Association of Thought to the dream he said: "Six-fifteen is the time mother used to put *me* to bed, and *she* was going to a party in her evening dress. That was when I was four or five. How could one like a mother that left one and let herself be taken away by father? The machinery was almost human in its desire to start before four o'clock! The man who started it up is a very natural fellow. He doesn't take much notice of rules and regulations but does what he feels. This compensating-instrument-business

H

which I do in conjunction with President Roosevelt associates in my mind with the idea of some ego-adjustment of sexuality.

"Now I remember I had a dream just before the one I have told you. It was about a gentleman I know and his son inviting me to dine with them. I felt very pleased. The bar in the restaurant was shut and you couldn't have any drinks but I did not mind that at all. It suggests to me that I am linking up father and son and I am indifferent to the bar (drinks, i.e. *woman*) being shut to me. I am linking myself up with father and that puts mother to bed! She is done with. You can afford to do this if you have got father friendly and then you can get on with the power-house-potency. Four o'clock, well that is my age, four years. You could even control the variables—provided Roosevelt is with you. You have got to get your own potency adjusted first—no fear of crocodiles."

Interpretation: From being the son, he has in this dream turned the tables and taken the mother's place. *He* goes off to the party as *she* used to do in her evening dress, with the father image, just as she did. He is not yet four and wants to start the sexual machinery working. It is clear that this patient at this very early age identified himself with his mother, the good object, the best thing he knew. As a part of this phantasy he links himself up with the father image, usurping the mother's place. It will be seen how closely this corresponds with his emotional pattern of linking himself up in real life with father figures and ignoring all women. He "puts them to bed" as he puts his mother to bed in the dream, that is to say keeps them *out* of his emotional life. This was the picture, and to some extent still is, but the son is changing; perhaps he is unrepressing emotional patterns which existed before he put the mother to bed and eloped with the father. At the next session he produces this dream:

"I am walking along a path with my mother. I am carrying a box with my chocolate rations in it, but there is a mouse in the box. Then standing in the path I see a curious form of wild dog with scales on it. I say to my mother 'Look, we will give the mouse to the dog! I bend down and offer the box to the dog and it takes the mouse into its mouth, but having demolished the mouse the dog then takes one of the pieces of chocolate. I tried to get it from the dog by hitting it hard on the back of the neck, but it wouldn't give it up so I lose that bit of ration."

He then remembers another dream which he had on the same night.

"Two new men have joined my firm. They are from my old college. One of them is called 'Work' (he doesn't know the name of the other!). Then I go upstairs to my Chief's last conference before his departure. He had had his notebooks cut up and the sheets distributed among the remaining staff. Suddenly he throws down his pencil and walks out of the room. He is gone. I stand up and say 'Isn't it amazing how quickly he has gone? Just nine months and that is the end of it. Still,' I say, 'he was better than the previous one' and then I proceed to mimic an imaginary conversation with the previous one. I say he would ask you the train to Banbury Heath and you would tell him the train would arrive at four o'clock and you would have to change. He would correct you and say 'no, at 4.10, but the connecting train waits.' I realized in my dream that Banbury Heath was an imaginary name."

In association to the dreams he says; "I have told you about the man and wife I knew who used to talk to each other on the telephone about chocolate rations meaning sexual intercourse. The dog with scales looks like that blessed crocodile again, only not so terrifying. It has become a much milder thing and what is more it has come out of the cavern. But now I seem to remember that in the dream mother and I were walking through a wood.

"The third dream is more a reunion . . . old college friends coming back. 'Work' is rather fun; I enjoy it. I enjoyed too the boss going. He was sad when he left. He throws up the sponge, his pencil . . . good heavens he has gone just like that! . . . all the fathers are going . . . the former one too . . . Banbury Heath . . . Banbury is where a friend of mine lives, a great man that I admire very much. I spent the week-end with him on several occasions at Banbury. There is no such place as Banbury Heath, but recently my mother told me that she intended to live in Bushey Heath. So I joined the two together, the father and the mother. The train goes to this junction of father and mother."

Thinking of the mouse, he says: "I don't like small living things, not even when they get considerably larger. I don't like pet animals and it is only very recently that I have been able to pat a dog. The mouse in the box is I think a very contemptible edition of the crocodile in the cavern and the same applies to the wild dog in the park, though not quite so contemptible. There is the dog barring the way to happiness with mother. Therefore I make friends with the dog . . . the father . . . what a marvellous solution to give it the mouse—its own little brother as it were, or a part of itself. The trouble is that the dog takes my chocolate ration as well, that is to say he is taking my fun, but not without a struggle. I tried to get my fun back . . . I could have got it back if I had taken it out of his mouth, but I was too frightened to do that. Here is the struggle all over again . . . happiness with mother and then this live thing, father's thing, in with all the sweets."

The concept of the "bad thing" in amongst the sweets, a classical concept in psychoanalysis, should remind us of all the similar phrases throughout the generations: the snake in the grass, the fly in the ointment, the serpent in the Garden of Eden. It is a concept evidently deeply rooted in the Universal Unconscious. But in this case the contemptibleness of the mouse in contrast to wild dog and crocodile suggests that it symbolizes his own infantile penis. If this is so the mouse amongst his chocolates would represent his own disquiet at genital sexuality having come to life and, through its pleasure-seekings with mother, disturbing his relatively conflict-free anal and oral libidinal pleasures. So he wants to get rid of it and give it up to father.

The patient continued: ". . . but I knew how to deal with it. I thought: 'let him (the father image) resume ownership of his own part, that is to say acknowledge father's potency by giving it back to him and then we will be all right.' But we were not because he took the sweets as well. Now I remember the piece the dog took was a stick of chocolate which none of us like, a part of the ration which I try not to accept. Now I remember only the other day a man friend of mine bought this chocolate ration for me and I gave him that very stick in return for doing the errand. He is an elderly man, a father-figure. Actually I call him "daddy" from a sense of humour. That rather clinches the fact that the dog is a father-figure. I had forgotten all about that until just this moment."

Analyst: "What took place emotionally only the other day is evidently, though perhaps on a minor scale, identical with what took place emotionally in your relationship to your father and perhaps mother during your infancy."

Patient: "That's what's so difficult to realize. Of course, it was all my own creation about them (my parents) and me."

Analyst: "Yet it was all felt by you and was being felt only last night during the dream. What is more it is still being felt in all your relationships. . . ."

Patient: ". . . With all men and women. I can see it intellectually. With a woman I am afraid of all this and with a man I am busy giving him the equivalent of my chocolate ration."

Analyst: "And, more deliberately, the equivalent of your mouse."

The patient was characteristically amusing in his associations to the two men friends in the third dream.

He said: "Isn't it funny that one was called 'Work'? I liked him. Of course I like my work better than everything else. It's the only thing I seem to have no conflict or difficulty over."

Analyst: "And what about the other man? What was his name?"

Patient: "I don't know. He was a cheerful and gay fellow. I did not pay much attention to him . . . can't think what his name was. I didn't seem to know him very well."

Analyst: "Come now, if the name of one is 'Work' what is the name of the other?"

The patient is at a loss!

Analyst: "You have said he was cheerful and gay."

Patient: "Of course, if one was 'Work' I suppose the other is 'Play' and that is what I am no good at . . . that's what I know nothing about . . . I don't even know its name! . . . I don't know how to enjoy life. However, perhaps I am preparing the ground as I certainly seem to be throwing out all the father-figures . . . at least in my dreams. Though in that long dream after throwing out the father I seemed to join him up with mother in that Banbury Heath idea where the trains connect. It seems on the whole though that the path has been cleared of fathers. I wonder if the forgotten dreams, the one's I can't remember, are more representative of my own union, or something, with the mother figure."

That this speculation was well founded was evidenced at the patient's subsequent session. Whatever the forgotten dreams may have been about, and they certainly seemed to be beyond recall, there was no need to worry for within a day or two he was giving ample evidence that the father having been dealt with, more or less, the mother was now coming into the picture. His current emotional life, particularly that involving his relationship to the persons around him, male and female, was still lagging behind his analytical metamorphosis, but no doubt it was early to expect drastic changes. He had throughout his life been so preoccupied in dealing with males, particularly with those older than himself, father-images, that he had had little or no libido left for intimate emotional relationship with mother-images, that is to say with women. That such emotional potentialities were nevertheless present had been evidenced even in some of his previous analytical material, but on the whole they were obscured, if not completely buried, underneath the greater urgency of his relationship to the father-image, to men. Now that this latter is becoming cleared away we see emerging, within his analysis, the more nuclear preoccupation, though still deeply unconscious. Enough evidence of it comes up to show us that the deeper problem is how to adjust his life with the mother-image, with the woman. This first comes to light in the dreams to which we shall presently be listening.

Chapter XI

Heterosexual Anxiety and Resistance

FREUD HAS DESCRIBED the dream as "the royal road to the unconscious." The following chapter will show that although in a sense it is the road to the unconscious the dream can, nevertheless, be used as an obstacle to that road.

The dream can be used for a double and contrary purpose. Whilst the dream, or more specifically its *latent content*, is an expression of what is going on in the unconscious the same dream, or more specifically its *manifest content*, gives us this expression in such a form as to hide completely from our knowledge the very material which it is in a sense blatantly expressing.

In the following session it will be seen that the patient goes even further than this. He uses his dreams almost deliberately to avoid expressing what is fundamentally in his mind. The dreams had little or no meaning for him. Therefore to him they were just a mask, a mask under which he could hide himself from his analyst.

I was rendered a little suspicious by the very perfection of his disarming tactics. He lost no time in laying himself down on the analytical settee and straight away announcing, in a most businesslike manner:

"I had two dreams last night. The first was as follows. I was standing beside a dry dock when a man approached me. He turned away and jumped into the dock, which was quite empty at the time; and I jumped after him. It seemed that I was more or less under an obligation to jump after him. There was some vague idea of catching him in mid-air and rescuing him . . . absurd of course. So down I went with him. The prospect of falling to the bottom was so terrible that I woke up.

"I went to sleep again and dreamt the second dream. In the second dream I was back in my college at Edin-

burgh with Ian Anderson. He was at Edinburgh with me
and I liked him very much. In the dream I said it was so
nice to be in the centre of the old college. We went into
his rooms. When we got inside he became very ill, in fact,
he became unconscious. The doctor arrived and proceeded to examine him. Then there was a funny little pig
or piglet that was very energetic and kept running about
the room and trying to creep out under the door. When
consciousness returned to Ian's eyes I felt very pleased,
over-joyed in fact, and I didn't know what to do I was so
glad he was reviving again. Then we got very close to
each other and he lay on top of me and I tried to get my
organ inside him. While doing that I had a wet dream
and woke up to find I had had one."

The patient's comments about these dreams were very
sketchy, far less abundant and comprehensive than usual.
He described the piglet as a pretty pig which appeared in
one of Emett's humorous books. Of Ian Anderson he said :

"He has never excited me sexually at all and its six
years since I have seen him, or even as far as I know
thought about him."

After a protracted silence, he said :

"Frankly I am bored with all this."

Although I knew the patient was using the dreams to
cover up material he would otherwise have to tell me, I
knew also that the dreams, unknown to him, deep under
their surface, would reveal the very material he was
endeavouring to cover, and perhaps much else besides.
Therefore I thought it best to humour his original resistances for a moment and to insist merely that he did Free
Association of Thought to the items in the dream material.

We started with what he had called the dry dock. I
asked him to think of that and to tell me what symbol he
thought it suggested to him.

He said : "Well actually it was not so much a dry dock ;
it was a graving dock, though I didn't call it 'graving'
to you because I didn't think you would know what the
term meant. Of course now 'graving' makes me think of

'grave.' It was a big hole in the ground and well it might
have been my grave had I not woken up in time. It was
the acute anxiety of the situation that woke me up. Of
course the hole in the ground is a female symbol. The man
who jumped into it in front of me was, must have been,
my organ. That is why I was compelled to jump in after
him. Then the anxiety arose. It reminds me now of the
anxiety I felt when that girl spent Sunday and Sunday
night with me and I suggested sexual relationship. As
soon as she accepted I cursed myself. I felt most uncom-
fortable. I felt 'whatever have I let myself in for now!' It
was most awkward and repellant. I asked her if we should
do it before supper or after supper. And then there were
all the other problems about where to undress, what
preparation to make, etc. etc. I hated the whole idea. It
was a most trying and anxiety-provoking piece of work.
Had it not been for you, for your insinuations, I would
never have done it, not with her, nor at that time.

"The second dream also had its anxiety patch, but it
turned out much better in the end. When we went into
the interior of the room Ian, that must be my damned
organ again, became very ill. In fact, he became unconscious. That's about what I felt in my relationship to that
girl, or rather I wished I were unconscious. The doctor
arrived, that must be you. I don't know what the silly
little piglet was unless it was my pre-pubertal virility or
potency, the only part of me that was not definitely
castrated. Anyhow, the castrated part revived, as it did
with the girl, and then I felt much better. Of course
actually while I was asleep and dreaming I was lying on
my back and therefore it was on top of me—and it had
revived all right, for the works all happened."

Analyst: "In the first dream the graving dock, the
interior of a woman, is evidently a grave or tomb from
which you awoke just in time to save the castration or
destruction.

"We might put the underlying mechanisms of your
dream as follows: Your libido or sexual instinct tries to

fulfil its aim, namely, the relief of tension or orgasm. The first dream using the feminine symbol arouses anxiety; approaching orgasm is equated with castration so that you wake up and the purpose of the libido is not fulfilled. In this form the dream fails to discharge your tension.

"However, you go to sleep again; the undischarged libido is still seeking its relief of tension, and this time, with the help of a masculine symbol instead of a feminine, you fare better although when the feminine symbol first comes in, namely, the interior of the room, there is a temporary castration, for 'Ian' becomes very ill. However, the doctor, the fruits of your analysis, helps to revive your unconscious potency with resulting pleasure—'overjoyed' you say you were. The libido has wakened up again, and this time by the symbolism of the male, without the female, your castration anxiety is avoided or evaded and the libido is able to fulfil its needs with consequent satisfaction.

"And now that we have dealt with the dreams perhaps you will tell me what you used these dreams to cover up?"

Patient: "You old blighter! Whatever I do you always hurl it back at me as though it were a defence."

I cut short the patient's tendency to argue along these lines by pointing out that the argument itself was a defence.

He said: "Oh well, on the way here I thought 'Oh blast this man Berg!' I didn't want to come today and I don't want to come tomorrow. I'm fed up with this life. I'm fed up with you."

Analyst: "What am I? What am I symbolizing? What is it that has this effect upon you?"

Patient: "You are a tantalizer. There was a hint in your interpretation the other day that my only solution would be to find a woman and marry her. I can't bear such a suggestion . . . the idea of having a woman and letting the rest of the world take care of itself . . . I can't bear this analysis because it seems to be pushing me into a woman."

Analyst: "Oh, so you can't bear me because I seem to

be saying 'Jump into the "graving dock" ' and you say 'Well, I may have been ill to come here to this man, but I'm not as bad as all that. I'll throw the man out instead. So, what you have done in this session is to come to me and throw me a few bones in the form of a dream. You say to yourself 'Oh that will keep the lion away, the silly fool likes bones. I don't. I can do without them. The dreams mean nothing to me. They are just rubbish . . . just bones. Let him eat them up and then he won't eat me. I myself will get away scot free.' So you see you have been using your dreams, at least on a superficial plane, as a pretence so that I would not find out what you have been doing over this week-end, or what you have been thinking, so that you can think yourself unaffected by this analysis. Had you got away with this as you wished, you would not have revealed what you had been thinking about me or about the analysis. I would just have been put off with this red herring drawn across my path—the two dreams. So now we can see why you plunged so immediately into these dreams. We can see also why you hate this analysis. It is because your symbol of the woman is a graving dock or a grave in which you will meet with your death, your doom, and I seem to be throwing you into it. I am no longer the good father. I'm a menace. Your father never said to you 'Get into mummy's bed or into mummy's body!' That would have provoked anxiety. What he did say was 'Get into my bed,' more like the latter part of the second dream. In his bed there was no anxiety. On the contrary, you seemed to gain confidence and hope from him. There was no 'Ian' becoming unconscious. On the contrary the doctor restored him, revived him and 'Ian' functioned, and your libido relieved its tension instead of being entirely frustrated by the terrific castration anxiety.

"That is why you feel you must escape me, escape the analysis . . . escape the woman, give it up, get out of danger. But at least you might as well know what you are doing and why."

This session is recorded to show that the patient like many others has dissociated the world of unconscious phantasy from his ego, his conscious world. He prefers to regard the former as unimportant, as of no consequence, and wishes to live purely in an ego world without the interference of this other. That, however, was a vain hope for it was a world in which tension could not be released, where anxiety must keep cropping up, arising from the depths of an unconscious phantasy which could not be modified unless it emerged into consciousness and became associated with his ego and subject to conscious correction.

When he approached the woman for the purpose of gratification or the relief of tension, as he did on the evening to which he refers, his relief was not possible in a pleasurable way, not possible unmingled with enormous castration anxiety, and this castration anxiety threatened to thwart all his pleasures and all his aims and to keep him from marriage and a satisfactory solution to his life. This anxiety springs from this very region of the unconscious to which his dreams also belong. Therefore it is only by bringing its sources up into consciousness and adjusting the two together that he can hope to achieve a satisfactory solution for his libidinal aim and for his nervous, physical and psycho-sexual health, and indeed for his entire life.

Chapter XII

The Problem of Anxiety

THE ANALYTICAL EXCERPT recorded in the last chapter again calls attention to the very intimate relationship between anxiety and sexuality.

The patient under review is in a certain degree of Anxiety State although this is far from being his only or even his main symptom. Perhaps I could put this remark better in the following way, namely, that whereas some patients show anxiety and perhaps nothing but anxiety in the forefront of their symptom-picture this patient does not do so. He has already converted his anxiety into various characterological and other structures. Nevertheless, it was during the course of analysis that the foundation of all these various structures, symptom-formations and character-traits, rose to a conscious level and it became obvious that this foundation is or was anxiety. The anxiety is here emerging.

During treatment attention has been called to the fact that his sexual life is imbued with this anxiety though its source is largely of an unconscious nature. When he tries on an ego plane to imitate the conduct of his contemporaries even to the extent of obtaining the companionship of a lady and endeavouring to have intimate relations with her, he finds to his professed astonishment that these relations are not so pleasurable as he anticipated, or rather that they are not so pleasurable as they evidently are to other young men. He is as puzzled as is the dog in the advertisement of a certain malt beverage who with its forefeet on the table is smelling at the glass and inquiring "What is it master likes so much?"

Things do not go really wrong until it comes to the point of actual sexual intercourse, Then there are all sorts of hesitations and delays. His ego has to take charge of the position. He debates with the woman whether they shall have sexual intercouse before supper or after supper, or whether they shall delay it until they go to bed, where they shall undress and all sorts of similar irrelevant details. Then there is the question of position for intercourse which presents his ego with a number of problems. Finally, when the intercourse is attempted he is not completely impotent, but that there is a considerable degree of impotence is revealed by the fact that he does not experience much pleasure in the act, that it is somewhat too quickly over, and particularly in the fact that it gives very little satisfaction either on an instinctive or on an ego plane. The net result of this situation is that it is his general habit to avoid any intimate relationship. He never falls in love. He steers very clear of that. It would incur far too many dangers. On the whole he tends to disparage women and to laugh at the idea of joining up one's life with "such a person." However, all these are matters which we have discussed at previous sessions.

At the session here to be described there was at first no mention of his sexual problem, if it could be regarded by him as a problem at all. On the other hand, he arrived with the announcement that he had drunk a lot of whisky before coming to his session. It becomes quite clear that this, like alcoholic indulgence in general, was a defence against anxiety.

He said: "I drank the whisky because I was coming to see you."

Analyst: "What are your emotional relationships to me?"

Patient (after a silence and a struggle with himself): "I want to strangle you!"

After another silence he adds: "But even then your ghost would haunt me."

Presently he is seen to be quietly weeping upon the settee. Then he says:

"Yes I would, I would strangle that, the ghost too."

Analyst: "Then what? Would you then be free? But what are you crying about?"

(Silence.)

Patient: "General exasperation."

Analyst: "Are you crying because you have strangled me or because you haven't?"

Patient: "I know I never would strangle you physically, though I'd very much like to. In other words you have won a battle which I insisted upon joining."

The patient continued: "I think you have been fairly consistent all the time. Gradually I've got myself into a position that I'm very much affected by you and by everything you say. It seems you have become part of my life whether I like it or not. And I don't like it. I hate it. I'll have to strangle you."

Analyst: "Why?"

Patient: "Because I don't trust you. I feel you are unreliable."

Analyst: "What makes you feel that I'm unreliable?"

Patient: "Because you don't respond emotionally. I can never be sure of your sympathy if I need it. The only thing to do is to strangle that person. There is no other way out. It's my life or his."

Analyst: "Who is this unseen intruder who dominates you without having your trust?"

Patient: "It obviously fits the parent-figure. It might be a very nice situation if it wasn't for the lack of trust."

Analyst: "In other words it's all very well to be in somebody's hands, but its important to know that the hands one is in are those of God and not those of the devil."

The patient is in a state of anxiety which presents itself as a struggle between him, for his independence, on the one hand and on the other some externalized bad-object at the moment taking the form or shape of his analyst. This bad-object apparently has a great deal of unwelcome power over him.

At the session immediately preceding the present one he had given me a short dream which was that his mother and father were having a row with each other.

"In the course of the row," he said, "Mother died, or

seemed very submissive. I can't tell quite which, but apparently there was not much difference." It would seem from his present transference situation, his present relationship to his analyst, that he is in the role of the mother-image and the analyst in the role of the father. He is being made very submissive, or being squashed, fathered or killed by this superior figure to whom he does not attribute unqualified benevolence and in whom he has not complete trust. That is why he "dying," feels he must strangle him, in order to preserve his own life.

Nevertheless, at the present session the problem of anxiety is carried to a deeper or more nuclear level by his sudden recitation of the dream sequence of the immediate night before.

"There was a series of four dreams," he said. These dreams bring out, perhaps to our astonishment, again the very intimate relationship between anxiety and sexuality, and therefore they make us face up to this problem in its basic form. The dreams were as follows:—

1. "I was going up a river, following its course, yet I was on an island in the river. The river looked very beautiful. The banks were most luxurious. There was a sort of voluptuous feeling in the dream. But I couldn't go any further because I was on an island in the river. There were a lot of people sleeping on this island."

In Association of Thought he related the voluptuous feeling in the dream to the voluptuous feeling of sexual intercourse, particularly of its early stages. The river he concludes must be a vaginal symbol. The island he concludes must be the womb indicating that the dream has reference to mother-fixation, and the inability to go any further is due to incest-taboo. "I, multitudes of me [a lot of people—indicating emphasis], am sleeping in the womb."

He says: "There was no anxiety, like there was with Phyllis, *because* I did not proceed."

Then he goes on to tell me the second dream.

2. "I was in some great hall and there was to be a

I

great organ recital. It was to be an all-day recital and everybody was sitting there most interested and most intent."

Of the "great hall" he says "Again the interior of mother." At the thought of the "great organ recital" he bursts into laughter and says "Father was to perform and I was most interested and intent. Evidently I got my sexual excitement by proxy. That is how I avoided anxiety.

"The third dream was more interesting. There I began to do something myself. And anxiety arose."

3. "In the third dream there was a large pier like one gets at the seaside. I think it was at the seaside. There was a low platform under the pier near the level of the water, the platform from which fishermen fish. It was as usual made of iron grids or something, very precarious and uncertain. I was on one of these very low platforms and the water was level and it came splashing through. Also there was some ice. It was difficult to walk along it. I was in great danger of slipping and being washed away into the sea. Anyhow, I got to the shore in the end. When I got to the shore I went through a hedge and found my way into a house. I had a terrible job in finding the opening in the hedge that led me to the house."

He associates his anxiety in this dream to the identical feeling of anxiety which he experienced during a recent act of sexual intercouse. Regarding his danger of slipping and being washed away into the sea he admits that even quite early in this sex act he felt that his anxiety might cause a premature ejaculation before he was ready, that is to say before he had mobilized his libidinal tensions preparatory to an adequate orgasm or satisfaction. However, he negotiated this danger, had some difficulty in effecting complete intromission ("terrible job in finding the opening in the hedge") but achieved it ("found my way into the house").

The fourth dream is even more highly charged with anxiety and it reveals that the termination of his sexual tumescence was a castration phantasy and not a true or satisfactory orgasm.

4. "I was in some large interior like a theatre. I was on a balcony looking at the stage show. The balcony was very high and sloping down towards the stage; also there were no railings round the edge. I was sitting on a chair at the very edge of this balcony and I could have slipped off as easily as anything. I sat there looking over on top of the stage. On the stage there was a little black man dancing very vigorously. When I saw him over the edge I kept wondering whether it was safe. Then I thought to myself: 'I'm not afraid of heights any more. If somebody does come along from behind and push me it won't matter because it is a long enough drop to kill me.' Some people, including that great man whom I know, came along to join the party. That was the end of the dream."

The patient then adds: "I wondered if the dream ended there because when this man arrived, obviously a substitute for you, I was afraid he was going to push me off."

This dream shows that during his state of tumescence during the sex act, that is throughout the time while he is watching the little black (i.e. anal) man (phallus) dancing vigorously, he is experiencing the anxiety of premature ejaculation (i.e. castration). His fear of height is of course the familiar fear of castration resulting from tumescence.

Before we concentrate on the interpretation of this series of dreams as a whole it will be as well to mention the actual analytical situation at the moment. This patient had reached such a state of anxiety during his analysis that he had at this point, unknown to his analyst, suddenly volunteered for commando duties. (Fortunately for him and for the progress of his analysis he was rejected.) To justify his action he brought up all the usual rationalizations—that at this stage of the war it is unpatriotic, foolish, in fact unjustifiable to go on attending daily for analysis when the country is at stake. It is obviously his duty as a Britisher to volunteer to beat the enemy and to leave his analysis to after all that.

The interpretation of this attitude of mind and of his behaviour is, of course, clearly that it is not the particular stage of the world war to which he is referring but the particular stage of his intrapsychic "War." He is approaching such terrible things in his own unconscious that it is far preferable to face similar terrors in the real world. In short, he is fleeing from the id-domain in which lives anxiety to get into a relatively safe ego world, albeit this relatively safe ego world is one of bombs, shells and fighting; thus showing us that there is, of course, no escape from the id! We have made the external realities correspond to it. Nevertheless, *real* dangers, *real* explosions, just kill you, you feel nothing; therefore they are much preferred to unconscious dangers of feeling all the terrors of the nightmare which lie within the id. Thus we see that dreams are not a thing apart from our real world in which we live. The world of the nightmares is felt to be far more dangerous, though actually the real world is a pretty fair representation of it.

Some degree of psychological impotence, or of prematurity of ejaculation, is seen in the light of this series of dreams to be due to the castration anxiety of incest phantasies. The mother- and father-fixation of his libido is so great that any attempt at sexual intercouse acts as a stimulus to the unconscious phantasy that he is entering the mother's body, as the infant evidently phantasied in connection with the development of his genital libido, and that in performing this entry father or father's phallus would castrate or destroy him. Hence intense anxiety is inevitably associated with heterosexual experience, and this will be so until the original Oedipus phantasies are brought fully into consciousness and their affects cathected, and until he is enabled to dissociate current sexual experience from its infantile patterns.

Until this can happen every woman is apt to symbolize mother, and every sexual tendency towards her to activate the anxiety of castration at the hands of father. This danger is relatively though not always completely avoided by restricting the process to phantasy with its unconscious incest phantasy, and the act to masturbation.

The problem of anxiety is still the nuclear problem of medical psychology. It is evidently a problem which hampers the mental functioning of the psychologist as well. as that of his patient, for ever and anon he is forgetting how intimately mixed up it is with the problem of sexuality, until, again and again, this close relationship is revealed to him by some material straight from the patient's id. Such material may be a *symptom*, for example that of impotence, or relative degrees of impotence, on the one hand, or very often more directly, *dream material* such as that here detailed which suddenly emerges and throws at least some light upon a problem with which both he and his patient had been fruitlessly struggling.

Wilhelm Reich has made a whole volume revolving around this subject. He has called attention to the antithetical functions of the sympathetic and the parasympathetic nervous systems claiming that there is an actual anatomical and physiological basis for this intimate relationship or antithesis between sexuality and anxiety. While he emphasises that sexuality is centrifugal in its distribution of libidinal energy, centrifugal because it goes out from the individual and impresses his environment both materially and biologically thus resulting in reproduction of its kind, anxiety on the other hand is said by Reich to be centripetal, the libidinal energy going in the opposite direction along the sympathetic paths causing various restrictive innervations of his autonomic nervous system and of the glandular or endocrine agenda, this last process resulting in all the symptoms with which we are familiar as those of Anxiety Neurosis or of the Anxiety State.

However, we are here concerned more with the *psychology* of anxiety, specifically with the anxiety and inadequate potency of this particular patient, than with its possible physiological mechanisms.

We have referred to the tendency in this patient to actualize his conflict, presumably in the hope of escaping from it into real-world dramatizations, by volunteering for commando duties. In the next chapter we shall see that even in the absence of belligerent facilities he, together with the majority of persons, tends to actualize it, particularly its castration elements, by unconsciously motivated acts or accidents. It may be suggested that the mechanism of this process is not unlike that of the production of hysterical conversion symptoms in which latter the castration is symbolically presented even in the absence of the "accident" or unconsciously motivated act.

Chapter XIII

The Psychology of Accidents

MANY SO-CALLED normal persons have in the course of analysis discovered to their amazement that within or beneath the cloak of normality their psyche conceals all the ingredients of every psychopathological formation and mechanism.

The patient whom we are studying was far from belonging to that large group of psychopathic persons who are constantly meeting with accidents minor or major, nor was he in any sense a true conversion hysteric. On the contrary, he did not succeed in freeing his ego from mental embarrassments in the way that the conversion hysteric is such an expert in doing. His ego was unfortunately cluttered up with its own conflicts and mechanisms.

Nevertheless, a minor episode had recently arisen during his analysis the source and mechanism of which we had not at the time succeeded in bringing fully into consciousness. Our opportunity arose later.

The episode to which I refer was that of an occasion on which he had said goodbye to a married woman in his relationship to whom he had achieved a greater degree of transference than he had ever previously experienced towards any female. There had been many elements of the mother-pattern in his emotional relationship to this woman. For instance, most unlike all his previous experiences with the opposite sex, he had to his astonishment taken the trouble of journeying half-way across England to spend a Sunday with her. When he arrived at the meeting place she had jocularly thrown him a parcel. In his surprise and amazement this had slipped through his fingers and fallen to the floor. This can be interpreted as her offering sexuality to him, and his failing to take it. Contrary to all anticipations his day with her, despite fine weather and a country ramble, had been one of unrelenting embarrassment. Even attempts at mild flirtation had proved sterile, despite the fact that only a week previously their relationship had been most intimate.

Shortly after arose the occasion for the final parting. It took place in London. They had spent an evening together. She had informed him that her husband was due to return the next day and this was their final meeting. He professed to himself, and to me later, that as usual such an announcement barely touched him emotionally. But nevertheless he had hardly left her when he partly fell down the tube escalator and sprained his right ankle. In spite of all attempts to disregard the accident the swelling was visible as he lay on the settee at his next session and he could not succeed in concealing the pain and the limp even from himself. This had happened notwithstanding the fact that his main transference was not to her but intra-analytical.

A few weeks later he was contemplating his final adieu to his analyst. He was being drafted abroad, a contingency which he might have avoided in favour of continued analysis, but which he had inadvertently solicited during a negative phase. This negative phase leaked through despite his attempts during the session to conceal it.

He began his session by a highly intellectualized attack upon my conduct of his analysis and a succession of accusations against me to justify some alleged lack of progress. Presently it transpired that he had had a dream in which he had appeared in a criminal court proceeding as counsel for the defence. He was carrying a large sheaf of papers which was his brief to prove that no crime had been committed. I pointed out to him that we had had enough of the defence; now we had best hear what was the crime. The defence continued. As it threatened to absorb all the time at our disposal, I cut in with a definition of the crime as that of patricide or matricide. After a short silence he admitted:

"There is a lot in what you say. In fact, when I left you last night I got half drunk and all the way home I was saying to myself 'I have got to kill him [the analyst].' "

I said: "The hate side had won for the time being." I added, "If letting out your emotions entails the death (i.e. murder) of father or mother you would be careful not to let them out."

At his next session he remarked: "Last time I wanted to kill you, and since then there are two things I have found myself thinking about. One was when I go abroad, how on earth am I going to say goodbye to my mother. And the other was a sort of puzzled wonder whether I really was going away for good and not coming back to you ever. Then I found myself thinking or hoping that England itself would be blotted out; the Germans would stage a counter-invasion and that would be the end of England for ever. Suddenly I realized that it was not just you that I was killing,—I was killing the whole of my past . . . all my traditions. I suddenly realized that I had discovered that sitting here and being surrounded by past associations, fixated to the unalterable emotional patterns of my past, did not lead anywhere at all. It would all have to be played out and destroyed before I could start the new life afresh.

"After that I was suddenly seized with an intense anxiety regarding how I would fare without you. This anxiety was present because I feel more helpless than ever, and even less capable of being helped."

Analyst: "Has that situation existed before?"

Patient: "Yes, it was a situation that made me part company with my mother at the age of twenty."

Analyst: "And what happened to you then?"

Patient: "That is when I started to accumulate this illness. Something was dying, and yet I was determined that at all costs I would do without mother. I gradually ran down like a clock . . . until I came here. In fact, that is why I came here. I would not go back to mother though something was running down or dying. Life, or something like life, was petering out. I would not go back to mother, but I did what was psychologically the same thing. I came here to you instead."

Analyst: "And as you broke away from mother so you are proposing to break away from her again, only this time the new mother in the shape of me. If you were going to do this why did you ever come to me?"

Patient: "Perhaps I hoped that you would make me a self-winding clock."

With the continued postponement of his departure further sessions became possible.

So far we have obtained little insight into the psycho-pathology of accidents or of conversion hysteria, but it comes in this next session.

He began in his characteristic way by bluntly stating:

"I do not feel that there is any point in my going on coming here."

Having elicited no response from his analyst, after a considerable silence he continues:

"Yet I don't want to stop coming. The whole thing is hard to imagine. I find it hard to imagine leaving here at all. I feel that something has eluded me. I have not got the answer which I have been seeking. You may be right in thinking that I form strong emotional attachments, but the point is that I am not *conscious* of them. For instance, I think I may have a strong emotional attachment to you, but I am not conscious of it. I fancy that it may arise when the moment comes to say goodbye to you. Then something dreadful may happen. Anyhow, the emotional attachment is not a source of pleasure. It will just be an ache at the break."

His ramblings seemed to take on a defensive measure and not to be leading anywhere and so I asked him directly for Free Association to the feeling that "there isn't any point in going on coming here."

He said: "It is a kind of frustrated feeling, so frustrated that I feel I might as well close down on it now. It just occurs to me that it is the end of my last lingering hope that you may respond."

Analyst: "What we want now is your phantasy of my responding."

There were a lot of defence-resistances to the production of this phantasy, but I was unrelenting. I said to him:

"You have become conscious of, and told me of, the affect of a certain phantasy, the affect being the feeling that there is no point in going on coming here. This is the sequel to a feeling of frustration and the end of a hope that I will respond. All that is missing is the phantasy from which these affects emanated. Let us have it."

Patient: "Well, I feel that you are holding out on me and that by responding you would be ceasing to hold out on me."

Analyst: "Association of Thought to the feeling that I am holding out on you."

Patient: "Oh, we have had it before a hundred times and I have given you Association of Thought to it at least once before so it is waste of time to repeat that."

Analyst: "Would you cease to kiss your wife a second time, or a hundred times, because you had done it once before and it did not lead to anything?"

Patient: "Yes, that is why you would cease, because it did not lead to anything!"

Analyst: "And so you object to becoming conscious of the phantasy of my responding because the phantasy does not lead to anything. I will give you at least the outline of the phantasy. You are looking for orgasm with the parent-figure and no other orgasm will suffice. You probably get nearest to orgasm with the parent-figure when you masturbate, and that is why you prefer masturbation (i.e. phantasy orgasm with the parent) to sexual intercourse with a non-parent."

Patient: "Yes. Quite."

Silence.

Analyst: "What have you been keeping to yourself for the last five minutes?"

Patient: "I had a hell of a day-dream then of creating a scene at the last session, a terrific scene, so that you would say it was impossible for me to go. But after that little phantasy I thought to myself you would probably be as heartless as ever and therefore I would be as steady as ever."

Analyst: "And give no orgastic display?"

Patient: "Quite. Yes, I see, the hell of a scene would be the orgastic activity."

Analyst: "An hysterical orgasm?"

Patient: "Yes."

Analyst: "Is this 'being-as-steady-as-ever' a sample of what you are doing emotionally throughout your life and doing it just because the analyst or the parent is likely to remain as heartless as ever?"

tient: "Yes."

Analyst: "And you are going even further than that and telling yourself that you actually feel nothing."

Patient: "Yes, that is it."

Analyst: "You spoke of creating a scene. Let us have your Free Association to that."

Patient (after an interval): "My first difficulty is to know what I would do. I do not feel that it is connected with you. That is to say I don't want to hit you or do anything to you. I think of something violent, bursting my lungs, or putting my finger up my nose so that it would not come down again, or losing control so completely that I can't get back to normal; losing the use of my limbs such as straining my muscles so that I could not stand, or a paralysis. But it is worse than all these, or better as far as emotional gratification can go, because it is something dynamic. For instance, you kick out your legs so violently that you break your knee . . . something so violent that you could not do it with your ego . . . my ego could not make me break my knee, but once it was done, *then* you would have to take charge. You would have to report me as unfit and under your medical care."

Patient (after a pause): "But I know I would not do

it because I am too much under control. I would never let myself out as much as that. I might get as far as sobbing on the pavement outside, but that is all."

At this point I reminded him that his ego had not always been so completely in control. It was only a few weeks ago at an emotionally similar parting that he fell down some stairs and actually did achieve a physical disability and that violently induced, namely, a sprained ankle. Had he done this a little more completely and done it in the presence of the person from whom he was parting she would have had to take charge as she could not have left him lying prostrate on an underground railway platform. Then we would have had a complete demonstration of the phenomenon of hysteria or hysterically motivated accident.

"Yes, there would have been more gratification in that, but I don't seem to be able to pull off these forceful things with you, things that would enable me to get the upper hand. This is a most unsatisfactory disability on my part. You see, it cheats me of the satisfaction, orgasm if you like. While it is all in my mind, or in your notebook, you can still be impartial; but if only I could succeed, if only my ego would get out of the way and let me do a thing like this, a violent thing, if only I were paralysed all over, then you would just have to do something. That would fetch you at last. You would be compelled to pay attention, to take me seriously, in fact so seriously that I would have no other course but to go on coming here. You would have to write to the military authorities to say that Martin had paralysis and could not go on duty till he got over it, but the great triumph for me would be that I had forced you."

Analyst: "You would have got the parent-figure down that way."

Patient: "Exactly. Though I would be paralysed I would have succeeded in my determination to dominate, and particularly to dominate you. Perhaps it is of interest that my method of domination is to paralyse myself."

Analyst: "So we have your phantasy. That is how you make the parent-figures participate in your orgasm. Or if you don't see it as an orgasm you can at least see it as a crisis. It is your crisis and you force it on them and they are forced to respond to it. It is your crisis, but the parent-figure has a crisis too."

Patient: "I am thinking of what my mother has said of me when I was very small. She said 'you were a very determined little boy, but I would not give in to you. Somehow I realized that it would have been bad for you if I gave in.' I wonder if she was right. Perhaps if she had given in I would have learnt that I only had to get in a sufficiently bad temper and I could rule the world. Perhaps I would have grown up into a person who ruled all those around me by bouts of temper." Reflectingly: "Such a person, if he comes up against it and cannot rule by temper may then throw a fit or some such all-compelling phenomenon. If all else fails he might even finish up by suicide.

"On the other hand it occurs to me that such symptomatic behaviour would only occur in a person who was excluded from more gratifying methods of tension relief. For instance, if he did all these things on a sexual plane instead of in a reality or ego world he would be simply a normal male achieving sexual domination of the female and imposing orgasm upon her whilst achieving it himself."

The material of this session may give us a little insight into a number of mental phenomena ranging from accidents to fits, or even to suicide, in the absence of any emotional reaction on the part of the love-object to the most violent demonstrations of emotion. In particular I wished to draw attention to the rather vivid, if limited, insight it provides into the aetiology of accidents and of conversion symptoms in hysteria.

Whilst the patient was feeling his way to a description of his formerly unconscious phantasy of forcing me, his analyst, to respond to his emotions, it struck me that he was providing one of the most vivid and colourful descriptions of the motivation and mechanisms of accidents and of hysteria which I had seen. Several causative and contributory elements are involved.

(1) Is a frustration of orgasm; (2) a frustration of the wish to arouse response in the parent-image or love-object; (3) a release of the accumulated orgastic tension in the form of a violent act; (4) this violent act is introjected, or at least exercised on the person of the patient himself; (5) whilst it succeeds in reducing the tension, it succeeds at the same time in a symbolical expression which includes the castration element inseparable from incest (e.g. breaking the knee, or achieving complete paralysis); (6) and, perhaps most characteristic of all, it overcomes the frustration embodied in (2) in that it forces the parent-image to enter fully into the emotional situation and himself to become a victim of the crisis, thereby not only making him a participant, but wreaking revenge upon him for his persistent impartiality.

Over-determination of the symptom is thus apparent. The hysterical patient in his symptom-display, particularly when of a conversion order, is succeeding in all these libidinal aims and is at the same time freeing his ego from the hampering or immobilising effects of an intolerable conflict. In its place he gives his ego only a physical disability to endure.

Chapter XIV

Analysis and Money

HITHERTO WE have been considering actual behaviour, symptomatic and otherwise, which can be shown to have its unconscious sources in the object-relationships characteristic of the Oedipus complex. It is only when the infant psyche has reached the relatively high stage of development described as genital organization of the libido that whole-objects such as his parents and other persons have mature libidinal meaning. As we have seen in the case of this patient such phenomena as hysterically-motivated accidents, sexual anxiety with its inadequate orgastic potency, and every aspect of transference are manifestations emanating from the one important unconscious nucleus described as the Oedipus complex whose whole-object relationships depend on a previous genital organization of the libido.

But this, although of outstanding importance, is not the only unconscious level from which symptoms and character-traits have their origin. On the contrary, pre-genital organizations of libido as evidenced in manifestations of the component instinct are often of great importance not only in the production of symptoms, but especially as the essential sources of character-traits and other peculiarities.

In spite of transference phenomena predominating in the analytical material, these manifestations of more primitive libidinal organizations must not be entirely ignored. Their difference is that their source is more in auto-erotic than in allo-erotic (object relationship) libidinal organization.

There is one of these in particular which analyst as well as patient is apt to consider entirely extra-analytical (as if any mental attribute could be extra-analytical!) because its reality relationship is of such manifest importance.

Whilst it is characteristic of psycho-analysts to regard all symptomatic behaviour, if not behaviour as a whole, as emanating from the unconscious and chiefly of value from their point of view as a revelation of the content of this unconscious, in this particular sphere the analyst himself is apt to forget the general principles upon which the whole science is based.

The blind spot to which I refer is the monetary relationship of patient and analyst. No doubt it is because in the sphere of money the patient is to give and the analyst to receive that both are apt to be rather shy about the subject. Their attitude is "the less said about it the better." It is as though they had made a pact between them to protect each other from the embarrassment, the emotional disquiet, of discussing this subject. If such an attitude were detected on any other subject, for instance that of sexuality, the resulting position would be manifestly absurd. But here, of course, the analyst is not expecting to receive sexual benefits at the expense of his patient. Therefore he sees the absurdity. On the question of money his own interests are touched and he adopts the usual defensive methods common to all. It will be readily agreed that any such defensive measure is the antithesis of analysis and must inevitably ensure the preservation of at least some portion of the psyche from analytical investigation. I hope in this chapter to reveal that it may ensure the preservation of the whole of it.

The patient we are here considering whose symptomatology and characterology were in direct contradistinction to the majority of our patients—based entirely upon an overwhelmingly strong ego and a correspondingly overwhelmed id, so much so that in the sphere of pleasure and indeed as a guide in life's activities he could never appeal to any feeling or impulse but had to resort to ego-planning and reason— suddenly exhibited what in his case could only be regarded as an amazing phenomenon, namely, that of total disregard for his monthly account.

K

Further, he took to writing comic messages upon this account such as "I am sure you will agree that these bills of yours are utterly unimportant, and that they may be completely ignored. O.K.?" and returning it to me.

Recognizing that profound analytical material indicative of ego-modification lay behind this new development, I awaited its emergence. He began by adopting the somewhat unconscious defence of plunging into analytical material. He followed this up by the detailed recital of no less than four dreams. After that he took recourse to an adverse criticism of the progress of his analysis, first suggesting that he should "give it a rest" and then adding that he did not feel that would be any answer. The very disjointedness of the session so far indicated that everything was beside the point, the point being the current emotions of the moment. He concluded with the remark "Of course I could go on coming here each day and wasting my time and yours, but I don't see the point of it. You can take a horse to the water, but you can't make it drink."

Analyst: " 'Horse,' proceed to drink!"

The patient was silent.

Analyst: "Why are you so particularly resistant today?"

Patient: "*I got another statement of your account yesterday.*

"The money I put aside for analysis is finished and my problem is: will the boat sink [apparently it has sunk] before I get to the winning post? What I mean is will my finances give out before my analysis is complete?"

He continues: "One of the rules of the game is that you never say how long the process will last. All one can get from you is just the idea that I should abandon myself to it. To this I say 'no fear, I am just going to pack it up.'

"I don't *want* to stop, but I think at times so long as there is money in the bank you don't care how long the analysis lasts. Your assumption seems to be that what you are giving me is beyond cost! I say 'to hell with that.' I cannot be sure that I am getting what I am paying for. This is the subject that is on my mind all the time. I am compelled to think of it. I feel that your whole attitude to the money situation is suspect, and therefore the whole thing, all the mumbo jumbo of analysis, is suspect. This, the sensible part of me, has come to life. Now I recognize that there is a non-sensible part of me that would like to lean on you, to rely on you like a child upon its parent. The difference is this—whereas in the child-parent situation the child receives and the parent gives, this is a situation in which the parent takes and the child gives. I am not going to be sold any longer. My reality sense has at last come to my rescue.

"However much I want this thing, however much I enjoy it, I shall treat it as I treat all my other enjoyments in life, on the basis of pay-as-you-go, and if you can't pay give it up. If one wants a thing strongly enough one will always find a way of getting it, but my idea is that if your want is expensive give it up and go without. I have always led my life on the principle that if I cannot afford a thing I had best give it up.

"Of course, I must admit that analysis has shown me that that is the essence of what is the matter with me. I have cured myself of wanting practically anything and everything in my life. That is why when work ceases on Saturday I am at a complete loss to know what to do with my spare time. In this way the ego is my life, and there is, in a sense, no life. I recognize that I have been only too successful in keeping all my wants out of consciousness. Perhaps it is for this same reason that I am at a loss immediately I am released from the ego-compulsion of work."

Analyst: "You are repressing your wants in order to preserve your money."

To cut a long story short the patient finally came to a point where he discussed details of his income, the amount he lived upon and the amount which he was able to put by for analysis. He said:

"Prior to analysis I had saved a small amount out of

my monthly income, but now it has all been absorbed, together with the current monthly saving. That is why I have not been paying your bills lately and that is why I have come to this crisis, or financial crisis, in regard to analysis."

It was, of course, a little tempting to take an active part in these discussions, especially as I had now been provided with the facts and figures. For instance, one could have suggested to the patient that he cut down his attendances to suit the amount which he had available monthly for this purpose, or offered other helpful suggestions. But it was already apparent that this subject was an integral part of analytical material and that it was safer to await his further Free Association of Thought. That this was the safer course to adopt was clearly revealed when he made reference to his inherited capital which he said amounted to the mere sum of £20,000. It had never occurred to him that any portion of this was available for use and therefore he had referred only to the net income accruing from it.

Patient: "When it is a struggle between wants and money, money has always won. I would not bargain with a proposed mistress as to what her salary would be; I would never doubt that it would not be worth the money."

Analyst: "Suppose we substitute 'wife' for 'mistress.'"

Patient: "A wife represents such a financial liability, such an expense, that it would never be considered. It seems I love my money much more than anything else."

Analyst: "Can we separate quantities of money or capital from quantities of *you*? Fluidity of the one means fluidity of the other and fixity of the one means fixity of the other. Money is a part of your psyche and therefore a part of the analysis itself. It is therefore analytically impossible to make rules about it."

It became increasingly evident that the patient had made for himself an ego world with his capital as the foundation and framework of it, and that the rigidity of the latter was an index of the rigidity of the former. I finally suggested to him the interpretation that the proportion of his capital which he was prepared to put into the analysis was an index of the proportion of his personality that he was prepared to change. Hitherto the proportion had been zero.

At his next session he proposed to open a separate bank account which he would call the analytical account. He would feed that account with his current savings, but when it grew to an overdraft of say £100 he would then realize capital to that amount and transfer it into the account.

I interpreted: "At that moment a piece of you will be cut off from the fixation and cast into the melting pot."

Patient: "I have thought to myself I will limit my expenditure on analysis to a total of not more than five hundred pounds which I can do out of income, of course, leaving my unalterable capital of £20,000 intact."

Analyst: "Leaving yourself of course unaltered and unalterable!"

Patient: "Well, if I spent a thousand pounds of my capital what good would that do?"

Analyst: "At a proportionate estimate I should say one-twentieth of the whole!"

Patient: "But in any case I could not possibly bear to part with any of my capital. It must have taken a lifetime to accumulate and it is now gathered up as it were all inside me, and it is an integral and unalterable part of me. And so it will remain until my dying day."

The importance of this identification of his money with himself and its analytical significance will become clearer in the course of the following chapter.

Chapter XV

The Self-Sufficiency of the Anal Character

THE ORGANIZATION of the libido at the genital level of infantile development, a level at which we have been engaged in our unravelling of the Oedipus complex both through the interpretation of transference phenomena and in our analysis of psycho-sexual anxiety, particularly in Chapters XII and XIII, is of course not the only level of libidinal organization. There is an even earlier history of libidinal development and fixations at erotogenic zones that exclude transference or object relationships. These are the auto-erotic component instinct levels, and important amongst them is that stage of early development when anal activities with their associated feeling-life comprise a considerable part of the pleasure of life and the incentive for living. It is almost a world of its own modelled in its pattern largely upon the world of oral predominance which precedes it.

Any person who is inadequate or subnormal in his transference relationships to the opposite sex or to his own, or who is more or less sufficient unto himself may be presumed to have left a disproportionate amount of his libidinal energies fixated at a pre-Oedipus level and in general that level will be largely oral or anal. With the consequent relative unimportance of object relationships there usually exists an undue degree of introversion.

The patient under consideration is in no sense an extreme introvert, as is usually the case in pronounced anal characters. On the contrary, he mixes easily and happily with persons of either sex and of every class, both singly and in groups or parties. Nevertheless, one of the difficulties, perhaps the principal one which brought him to analysis, is that, particularly in the case of persons of the opposite sex, he has no enduring interest.

He is quite happy to live in a flat by himself, or occa-

sionally with a male companion. He has women friends;
not that he seeks them, perhaps because they thrust
themselves upon him; but before he has been long in any
woman's company he finds her "rather a bore." He
wonders how he is going to get through the next several
hours with her, and this in spite of a total absence of
shyness on his part. He says it is just that he would feel
able to get on with his own thoughts and activities much
better if he were alone—if he "could be shot of this
woman."

No person is indispensable to him, unless it be himself.
He admits that he has never been in love, that in fact he
has never had any sort of intimate attachment to any
person of either sex. He says:

"I have come for analysis partly because I cannot even
imagine myself ever falling in love with anybody."

The suggestion that perhaps he is already in love with
himself gains enthusiastic assent.

What is it about himself that he likes so much?

The following dreams may give us an inkling. At the
same time I think they may throw an especially vivid light
upon the subject of anal erotism. In my opinion they
reveal to us that the earliest weeks, months or years of life
contain within themselves a drama as full of happenings,
as detailed, as pleasurable, as exciting, and as dangerous
as any which we can purchase between the covers of a
7s. 6d. novel. The only difference is that whereas the
characters in the novel are living their emotional patterns
in an external or social environment, the baby, on the
other hand, is living them all within the isolation of his
own skin, or perhaps more precisely at the orifices between this skin and the outside world.

The first dream sequence that throws light upon his
character is as follows:—

After a brief reference to material which suggests the
Primal Scene (showing that his emotional life is welded to
infancy and the sexual relationship of his parents), he
finds himself in a taxi with a charming woman, and soon

gets to a stage of sexual play with her. But it is not at all exciting; gets him nowhere; and begins to be rather a bore. So much so that he is not sorry to find himself in an upstairs room in a house in Poland. This he immediately interprets as the land of po's. He insists however that it is an *independent* Poland, where, he says, you use the po without interference from anybody. There is a greeting over the door welcoming him to have a happy time inside. Thus we observe a regression from the unsatisfactory genital Oedipus level back to the relatively unfrustrated anal level.

He is discussing submarine production (colloquially referred to as "shit") with a Polish officer, whose large bald head he immediately associated with bare buttocks. His papers are spread all over the floor, crumpled papers. A big, tall stranger walks across and he shouts "Look out! You must not tread on these papers." Apparently it was most important that they should not be disturbed. He associates them, on the one hand, with lavatory paper, and, on the other hand, with his childhood games spread out on the nursery floor. But, he adds, a curious thing in the dream is that shortly afterwards the papers were being blown about all over the place, and this did not seem to matter at all. The nursery game was over.

Then everybody began to go in to dinner, but he found they were all in dress uniform, and he was not allowed to go into the same room. He was not suitably dressed. However, he found a smaller room where you could dress as you liked. "So," he says: "I went in there and thoroughly enjoyed my dinner."

He has reverted from anal to the closely related oral pleasures—both autoerotic.

The first room he calls "the parlour or dining room" from which his parents excluded him. The second room is the nursery, where he could do as he pleased and gratify his instincts.

He then relates to me a little experience of that morning. He says he could not evacuate his bowels, because the woman housekeeper was washing the floor in front of the lavatory. He therefore went to his office and began work. But, somehow, nothing would go right. He says: "At the office I found I could not get on with anything. It felt as though something was frustrating me all the time. I don't know why it was, but just before I left to come to my session I had a good evacuation, and what struck me so forcibly was that my whole mental attitude changed immediately. I had been so very dissatisfied with my morning's work, and immediately after that evacuation I felt thoroughly satisfied with myself and with everything."

He continued: "My interpretation is this: the housekeeper woman stands for my mother, and *my* choice was to evacuate, whereas she was frustrating me. Therefore I felt frustrated all the morning. When I went to the lavatory and had my own way I felt that nothing was frustrating me any more."

Seeing that one of the characteristics of this patient was the absence of any intimate relationship with any other person, one rightly assumed that he would be unlikely to acquire any very strong transference to his analyst. This was borne out by the fact that after a few enthusiastic weeks of treatment he remarked that he thought his analysis was finished. There was no need to attend any further.

Sensing his intolerance to frustration, I remarked that he had best follow his *id* in this matter. He reflected that as he quite enjoyed lying here and *"doing his stuff"* he would come for a few more sessions.

At this session he himself interpreted his early idea of terminating the analysis. He said:—

"I got rapped over the knuckles through sending off my work without showing it to the boss. I felt he was no good . . . he didn't matter. Now I realize that for some days I have had the feeling that I was killing off all my fathers, and that lay behind my idea of terminating the analysis. I was killing you off, like all the other fathers. It was a perfectly id-ish development. Even before that I

have been busy killing off all my mothers. That was
brought to my notice by my feeling that women were
rather useless. I have usually thought that of them . . .
not wanted them about me. I think in early life my
mother ceased to be of much use to me, while father continued for some years longer, as he occasionally played
nursery games with me. But now it seems that I am killing
off the whole lot of them.

"I can't remember the next part of the 'po' dream, except
that it was full of loneliness. I did a lot of wandering about.
I had a sense of being lonely, entirely by myself. It was
after this that it seemed I was trying to get to the place
where the party was, and never finding it. Then I came
across two women showing off their legs to each other.
They ought to have been showing them off to me. I was
there trying to find my way to a country house. I went
through fields and kept shutting gates behind me. In the
course of this I turned back to shut one of the gates, and
there saw a lot of cows. There was another man with me,
and there was a cow-herd dealing with the cows. He was
a virile sort of man.

"Now the odd thing was the way in which he was
herding his cows. He was rolling them up into a great big
ball of cows and then this ball went rolling towards the
field where they were to be herded, that is to say, into the
field in which I now was.

"The man beside me remarked about it, and I gave a
topical dissertation or lecture like this:

" 'There are two ways of getting cows into a pen. The
first is the slow and steady way. This corresponds to my
normal conscious way of defecating, ten minutes after
breakfast, reading the newspaper leisurely. The second
way is the swift, sudden, impulsive method. That is the
way my friend does it. He seems to come out of the lavatory almost as soon as he has gone in.' That is how the cow-
herd did it, rolling them all into a great big ball, and then
rolling this ball through the gate into the cow-pen.

"The second way was much quicker. The only thing

against it was that it was dangerous. It was dangerous because they were apt to fall upon their calves and damage them. In the dream it was not calves, but a little foal. I saw this great mass of cows roll over the foal and I thought it would be damaged. But I was relieved to see it get up all right after they had passed.

"That was the end of the dream. I never got to the country house, but I am telling you that I got quite a little pleasure and a bit of excitement on the way. It was fun watching those cows rolling in a ball like this. And it brings it home to me that my pleasures are more those of bowel evacuation than those of intercourse with a woman. I think in the dream I gave up the idea of the party, and was quite content to watch the goings on with the cows. It was quite exciting and even a bit dangerous. It occurs to me that passing an enormous motion may hurt the anus. It is a dangerous operation. . . . Yes, perhaps the real fun is in the anus squeezing out the stuff. The penis is a poor second. The woman is not really necessary.

"Nevertheless, it seemed that the casualties were high in this method of herding cows . . . and perhaps, it would be if you used the anus like this for pleasure."

Here I asked him if he meant orgastic pleasure.

"Perhaps I did not get a pleasure as far as that. Here is a pleasure as far as it goes; it is not as deep as that. It is simply a partial feeling. I am satisfied with the feeling for what it may be."

Analyst: "What is the danger you refer to?"

Patient: "Damage to the penis if the sensual pleasure is going to be derived from the anus. But, you see, the penis is not damaged after all.

"But it doesn't make sense to damage the *penis* by evacuating the bowels. It seems more likely that the danger in passing large lumps (the ball of cows) is a danger of over-straining and damaging the anal sphincter."

The true interpretation of this extraordinary dream is

that the cow-herd this "virile sort of man" is a phallic symbol albeit identified with the "potency" behind a too powerful evacuation of the bowels. Thus we show that potency can be an anal as well as a phallic attribute.

In real life, the patient tells us, it is his male friend not himself who evacuates his bowels by the "swift sudden impulsive method." The patient himself on the other hand does not exhibit this potency either anally or genitally. His castration anxiety (c.f. his fear that the foal will be damaged) inhibits him, as it inhibits any real drive or incentive to life. At the same time it avoids a challenge to his fellow men so that like many anal characters he does not incur the aggression of others but on the contrary gives no offence and gets on very well in a passive sort of way with his fellows. His method of evacuation is a slow one, reading the newspapers, typically anal rather than phallic—specifically of the second anal (retentive) stage.

He goes on to give innumerable details of his sublimated anal activities, and the pleasure and excitement he derives from them. For instance, he talks at length of the great pleasure he derives from "messing about" with the draft of any letter or article which he may write. He says:

"I write quite quickly, just straight from my id, but the real joy lies in reading it over and over again, and in making little alterations and improvements before it is finally transcribed. The curious thing is that, even after it is transcribed, and even after it is weeks old, I can never bear to part with it. I hoard it till my desk and drawers are full of these bits of scribble. I am never hard up for a little fun and pleasure. I have only to take one of my old efforts out of the drawer, thinking to myself: 'Yes, Chris, *you* did this—all by yourself.' I would like to be able to put 'All my own work' over every one of the things I have done."[1]

He goes on to give another example, this time one which shows a sublimation of oral as well as of anal libido and their natural inter-relationship. Indeed it may be

[1] C.f. ". . . for ever putting the jelly into shape instead of eating it"—a symptom he referred to at his first interview. Page 10.

seen that the sequence of ingestion, alteration and production of material on a sublimated mental plane has a
causal relationship to its pattern on a primitive physical
plane.

He tells me that although he is a great reader, if anybody tries to push a book on him his immediate instinct is
to refuse it. His immediate Association of Thought is that
as a baby although he had a hearty appetite his mother
was always piling food on his plate and wanting him to
eat more than his appetite. Therefore in self-defence he
was more concerned with refusing. He may at a later
date himself pick up and read the book he has refused.
"With all my avid reading I periodically get to a place
where I don't want to read any more, in fact I can't
absorb it. Soon after that I will start writing one of my
interminable articles, only to go back to my reading when
I have tired of this."

Thus we see the alternation of ingestion and production
follows the same pattern in the adult's sublimated activity
as it did in the infant's equivalent physical activities.

In the light of this dream and associated material may
it not seem that, without these intellectualized equivalents,
the infant is living in a world of experiences similar in its
excitements and alarms and perhaps identical in the
details of its emotional patterns with those which subsequently give rise to our conscious thought, and what we
eventually project and actualize in our environment? It
would seem further that pregenital (e.g. anal) fixations of
the libido can be deduced from negative evidences as well
as from positive, and that it may be almost safely concluded in cases where there is some inadequacy in love-
object relationships.

This patient had shown us considerable evidence of
inadequacy in this respect. We well remember the incident of the lady in the punt which he so naïvely related
to me at his first interview. We well remember also the
incident of the picnic in the car where he provided a book
for himself and the girl . . . "so that there should be no

embarrassment in the course of the long afternoon."
These instances show that his instinct or incentive, at
least on the socialized heterosexual plane, left much to be
desired.

He engaged himself in these activities because he was
trying to test out what it was that other human beings
liked so much, imitating them to no avail. Finally he had
come to analysis.

On the other hand and in contrast with these failures
he was constantly bringing to me some fresh enthusiasm
for some occult cult or new found literature. He was as
voracious a reader as he had been a hearty eater in babyhood—mostly of subjects rather off the record. Incidentally that is how he stumbled upon psychotherapy. But
his inquiring tendencies did not end there

With the accumulation of analytical resistances he
diverted his libido into a succession of pseudo-scientific
directions. Of the mechanisms at work one or two at
least were clearly discernible. For instance, it seemed clear
that he was for ever endeavouring to use his ego to take
up the burden and function of life *in place of* the deficiency
of drive from his id. It seemed that being unable to
obtain adequate drive, direction, purpose and satisfaction of life from id drives, the ego had to be used as an
alternative. This may possibly be regarded as an intra-
psychic equivalent of the mechanism of displacement
upwards. Libido was displaced from id levels, where it
could obtain only inadequate outlet, to ego levels where
it strove for ego satisfactions and the solution of the purpose of living by ego activities and these alone.

At the same time, some satisfaction or gratification was
required by the libido in this new locus; in lieu of instinct
satisfaction he was endeavouring to obtain some emotional
gratification on the intellectualized level of ego interests.
These pseudo cultures offered him some prospect of relief.

The question arises in my mind as to how general may
be this mechanism; as to whether the widespread enthusiasm for a multitude of such cultures, pseudo sciences,

religions and superstitions may have their source in id repressions, inhibitions and frustrations, with a resulting deflection of libido into intellectual channels, but into intellectual channels which are still seeking the emotional relief denied them along instinct paths.

Are persons who exhibit enthusiasms for beliefs, 'isms and 'ologys exhibiting in their intellectual life an immaturity exactly equivalent to that which exists in their unconscious libidinal pattern? Does the prevalence of this tendency in adolescence point to its association with libidinal immaturity?

The popular attitude of tolerant contempt for the crank suggests that he is in general regarded as a harmless psychotic or neurotic; that like the neurotic or psychotic, he is seen to be suffering from a deflection of libidinal energy from instinct paths into symptom-formation. (One might add that the public who are so discerning of those who differ from themselves are equivalently lacking in insight where their own mass delusions are the emergent symptom.)

Thus beliefs, superstitions, "-ismisms" and "-ismologies" may be seen, like psycho-neuroses in general, to owe their dynamic drive to libido deflected from instinct sources, and, like all symptom-formations, to have their nucleus in immaturity of libidinal development or in sub-normal orgastic potency. Fixations at pre-genital erotogenic levels, such as the anal, are, apart from castration-anxiety or in addition to it, the main cause of inadequate orgastic potency and of the consequent inability to regulate tension in an anxiety-free manner without symptom-formation, substitution or sublimation.

We have observed that this patient's symptoms were more remarkable for their negative than their positive aspects. He complained not so much of any symptom, but rather of the absence of what might be described as the usual "symptoms" of normal man. He is here showing one positive tendency at least. That is a tendency to embrace almost every new quack cult, superstitition or religion of which he chances to hear, or the literature of which falls into his hands.

I could not help seeing, through the study of his case, a relationship between the absence of normal impulse and incentive on the one hand and the presence of these new-found, transitory, zealous enthusiasms on the other.

However, from a technical point of view there is a matter which if not more basically important is more immediate, and therefore at the moment more important because it is fraught with the danger of a premature termination of analysis. This matter is the accumulating negative transference, which the patient had sought to hide under cover of a diligent recital of his dreams (c.f. Chapter XI).

The analyst, having established himself as securely as possible in a positive transference situation, had not only allowed much of this to be analysed away by interpretation, had not only attempted the removal of resistances by interpretation, but had even made so bold as to attempt the removal of symptoms which included modes of libidinal satisfaction—in other words to achieve, at last, though never at first (vide Chapter II), some therapeutic results by modification of the patient's emotional patterns or illness. This invariably provokes the negative transference and joins the analytical battle.

Left to his own devices the patient would have concealed his accumulated negative feelings from the analyst. The analyst had brought the patient face to face with his phobias, phantasies and delusions. It was too much. Part of him hated the challenge and hated the man, and, if this hatred were not brought out into the open and dealt with, escape would have been the next move. Negative transference if not revealed and interpreted, like all libidinal forces that remain unconscious, leads to action, action the source of which may never be known to the subject himself. In the analytical situation such action is naturally the premature termination of treatment.

Chapter XVI

Transference Resistance—A Session

A TRANSFERENCE SESSION, particularly a session occupied principally with transference resistance, is perhaps the least likely to be found recorded in psycho-analytical literature. No doubt this is because the analyst is almost certain to be so completely preoccupied with dealing immediately with the red-hot material the patient is producing that he has no time or ability to record it verbatim on the spot. Yet all analysts would agree that transference sessions, particularly sessions of transference resistance, are the most vital of all sessions in analysis. They are found to represent the very nucleus of the patient's troubles. His conflicts *in statu nascendi* (in a nascent state) are being presented to us like the blacksmith's iron straight out of the fire, in the one condition in which they are malleable, in which his whole character can be adjusted.

Here is an instance—by no means the only one in this book—where I have, in spite of the unusual difficulty, made an attempt to record everything that happened during such a session of transference resistance. The following material is all completed within one session of one hour. It will be appreciated that it was not possible to record everything, but I may say that the greater part of the material, written down at the time, comprises four-fifths of what was said and no material has been added afterwards.

After the last session (this refers specifically to the session recorded in Chapter XI) at which the patient had thrown his analytical lion a few bones in the form of a series of dreams in an attempt to deflect his interest from himself, specifically from his negative transference state, I made an attempt to bare the real issues of the case by asking the patient: "What did you use your dreams to cover

L

up?" In spite of the concluding part of the analytical time being occupied in revealing that the patient had been at great pains to cover up the essence of his emotional state (at the same time revealing to a limited extent what the nature of that emotional state had been), in spite of this he showed that that emotional state had not been completely uncovered and exposed.

This impression was confirmed by the fact that the next morning the analyst received a telegram which stated peremptorily that the patient would not be attending for the succeeding two days. In such a patient as this who conscientiously kept every one of his appointments, there could have been no more distinct evidence of his un-analysed negative transference.

On the third night he arrived at his usual time, but as he had no appointment he had to be sent away to come back later. He showed considerable reluctance to do this, but nevertheless agreed and returned.

The first thing he said when he lay on the settee was "I could easily have come on Tuesday only I thought to myself 'I am tired of slogging up to London. I'm never in my own flat. I never get any of my own things done.'

"And so I sat in my flat all by myself for two successive evenings and I might as well confess that I got nothing done just the same. So I thought after all I might as well come tonight as I get nothing done when I do stay away. It occurs to me that that is the complaint in life for which I originally came to analysis."

Analyst: "*Your wife* is away *all* the time."

(Silence.)

Patient: "Yes, I see it. My 'wife' being my mother. Anyhow I have so tied myself up with engagements next week that it doesn't look as though I'll be able to come at all."

(Pause.)

"Actually I am indifferent as to whether I come here or not."

(If the patient has been rightly treated, if the analyst

has allowed sufficient positive transference to accumulate before attempting modification of the patient's psyche, he need have no anxiety regarding the strength of the patient's attachment to him, no matter what the latter's protestations and dissemblings may be. What is more he should know this, be secure in it, and unafraid *at this stage* to interpret boldly and freely.)

Analyst: "The indifference you mention is the especially thick armour plating. Having put it on in several layers you then say 'Well, now emotions can try their damnedest. They can shoot at me from any direction. I can't be touched. I can't be hurt.' That is your 'indifference.' "

At this point the patient produces the characteristic arguments which we are accustomed to during the stage of negative transference. He says for instance:

"I am indifferent to Chinese culture, to take one example. Would you say I put on armour plating to protect my emotions against that?" And so on. He ramps on for several minutes. I say nothing. But in the end he confesses:

"I suppose I do fight against it.

"To hell then! I confess I do fight against it. So what?"

Analyst (significantly): "So you had to come to me."

The significance of this remark, though it is hard to transcribe, was perfectly well understood by both patient and analyst. It meant in short that it was this psychological tendency of his to fight against the things that mattered most emotionally, which was responsible for his life being so empty that he had months ago to apply to an analyst to help solve his life's problems.

"So you had to come to me!"

Patient (with a sob in his voice): "My God! I'd never have started if I'd known I would get mucked up like this."

He is nearly crying.

Analyst: "Perhaps that's what you have been avoiding all your life . . . getting mucked up. What would be the opposite policy?"

Patient: "It would be constitutionally impossible for me to pursue any opposite policy. I couldn't for instance, march over the edge of a cliff deliberately. I remember two friends of mine used to drive their old car about in a field and they wanted to wreck it so they made up their minds to drive it straight at the hedge. They found when it came to the point that they just couldn't do it. So I just can't get nucked up, and I feel I'm getting mucked up by coming here. And yet it seems there's nothing else to do but just come, and the whole of the rest of my life is at a standstill while I do this. Yet it's equally inconceivable to say 'Goodbye Berg.'

"If you said to me that I was not to come any more I'd feel that the bottom had dropped right out of my universe. I'm in the toils. I know I can't break it. Yet here I struggle to no avail."

Analyst: "Suppose you did the opposite?"

Patient: "That's equally impossible. There's nothing to yield to . . . nothing that I can understand or think. Yielding to a person demands a response from that person. There's no response from you, so, of course, it's utterly impossible to yield. I can't let myself go utterly."

Analyst: "You still haven't said why not."

Patient: "Well, I can't be so vulnerable. I can't trust you. You might do anything."

Analyst: "For instance? What is it that I might do? Let us have your Free Association of Thought to that."

Patient: "Well, I suppose you might get me in such a position that I couldn't help coming. Then I'd be sort of trapped—in your hands for the rest of my life. You could make me mad, or anything you liked. You could muck me up completely."

Analyst: "Take off the rationalizations of the ego and we might say I could possess you, castrate you, or even eat you. The only question to be decided is is it anal, genital, or oral?"

Patient: "I don't feel it as any bodily function. It's a mental state. That's much more subtle . . . too interesting

and absorbing. . . . It gets my mind; that's what it gets
. . . getting dependent upon you. Fancy, finding you
indispensable! What a state to be in. To find that . . .
fancy that."

Analyst: "Nothing new about that. I am indispensable
—*and I always have been.*"

Here the patient begins to look terrified.

"Yes," he says, "There was always somebody indispensable whom I denied. Yes, I know. I'm pushing you
out *as before.*"

Analyst: "That's your trouble, that's your life."

Patient (laughs and cries): "That sounds all right here.
You make me feel an awful twirp, but when I go from
here I'm different. I feel 'To hell! He's not indispensable.
How ridiculous to feel for a moment that he should be.
Of course he's not indispensable. Nobody is indispensable."

Analyst: "When you go from here you carry a banner
with a characteristic slogan 'ANYTHING BUT THE TRUTH.
EXCELSIOR!' "

Patient: "And when I come in here I have to lower
the banner and I feel a twirp. But I'm damned if I'm
going to recognize that that is it."

Analyst: "What is it?"

Patient: "I knew you would ask that. Perhaps I mean
that what's indispensable is somebody to whom you can
surrender utterly, and be yourself with."

Analyst: "Saying that would be so gratifying, so very
gratifying that you fight against it, deny it."

Patient: "I might be ashamed of it. I think that's likely.
I would be whacked. I would have lost everything."

Analyst: "You'd be gobbled up! You're afraid I'd never
let you go again."

Patient: "And another thing is: I might never *want*
to go again."

Analyst: "And you never wanted to go in the first place
. . . the very first place. Quite early in your sessions you
said to me 'What is a mother-fixation? I will not recognize
it.' All your life you have practically said: 'If I shut my

eyes tightly enough it's not there.' That's your method. Anything but the truth! Similar to your indifference."

Patient: "Yes, that's it. I've done that all my life— primarily to get rid of the mother."

Analyst: "And we see it's there all the time because we find you've again got to shut your eyes to some relationship between you and me."

Patient: "Yes, throughout my life whenever I find myself getting an emotional relationship to a person I immediately start resisting, forming attachments however slender in every direction instead."

Analyst: "The alternative would land you in for a really passionate attachment."

Patient: "Yes. I couldn't. The same as I couldn't throw myself over a cliff."

Analyst: "So you spend your life fighting yourself . . . fighting your destiny."

Patient: "Yes, it's so silly, but of course I must be getting many little attachments instead, but nothing which does away with my ego control."

Analyst: "The logical conclusion would be a complete union without excluding sexuality. That is the sort of union that would bind you psycho-sexually, and enable the rest of you to be free to enjoy the so-called ordinary conscious-level interests of life . . . interests which by themselves do not count for very much but appear to count for everything, provided the essential emotional pattern is being adequately absorbed. In the absence of the latter position, nothing matters at all. And that's your life."

Patient: "It sounds marvellous in here, but it just doesn't work outside."

Analyst: "You came to me just because of that very reason . . . that you couldn't walk over a cliff (your words) . . . you couldn't let this happen. But you must see the developing natural tendency, the tendency to fuse your soul with another (indispensable) person—like the amoeba fuses with another of its kind to change approaching death into an abundance of life. You couldn't let it happen . . . that's why you were unhappy and with no interest anywhere, losing interest in life itself."

Patient: "I don't want to die just because of some silly woman."

Analyst: "The important thing at the moment is that you are resisting *me*, not the woman."

Patient: "Yes, that is so, I was hoping you would be put off that."

Analyst: "My job is to bring all this up to consciousness; and then like the good parent did, or should have done, deliver you back to yourself."

Patient: "Yes, but I don't think you could deliver me back to myself. Perhaps you couldn't deliver yourself from me. Perhaps I would be too strong for you . . . make demands of you. You might have to submit, to throw up your hands and say 'I can't deliver you back to yourself.' "

Analyst: "That would only be likely if I too were emotionally attached to you so that I couldn't do without you."

Patient: "I feel terribly disappointed now to think that you are not emotionally attached. I think to myself you ought to be. Can you possibly still be indifferent? Good God! what can you think of me all this time baring myself to you, giving you my very soul and you remaining indifferent? You can't be . . . you can't be . . . you mustn't be."

Analyst: "We do seem to be seeing the anatomy of love don't we!"

Patient: "Yes, it's a devil of an experience. No wonder I've fought all my life struggling to resist it!"

Analyst: "And we see also the price of resistance."

Patient: "Yes, I see that all my life I have paid the price of resisting my natural instincts. I have resisted what you call normal tendencies to exercise the natural patterns I had on another person. I can see that I have paid the price of my resistance to this natural process by a life of

loneliness and sort of purposelessness, not knowing what
to do with myself; and of course a general repression of
all my natural feelings. Yes, I can see that I have paid
that price all my life, and you call it the price of resistance.
But I can see also that I am paying a price at present for
the opposite, experiencing all these disturbances here. The
trouble is that I am getting nothing in return. I am
resisting an attachment to you, an attachment which you
do not reciprocate.

"Will that help me to get an attachment to a woman?
A sexual attachment perhaps; that's easy, but not a union
that would make life happy for me. And what sexual
attachments I have had have really been, as I felt, under
your 'instructions,' to tell you about it.

"I saw a pretty girl in the tube today and I thought
to myself 'Just to think that she's got a crocodile inside!'
I laughed to myself at that, but anyhow I did not feel
any tendency to become emotionally attached to the
extent of becoming dependent upon her! It seems to me
that that would be a worse tragedy than my present one
of purposelessness. Besides I have tried the stuff and it
doesn't get me anywhere.

"Look at that other Sunday with Phyllis. As soon as it
seemed that she was willing for the sexual intimacy what
happened to me? I got almost in a panic. At any rate
I had a very difficult job, and I didn't enjoy it at all.
And that was a case in which I was not really emotionally
involved, just the surface, and I think not even that when
it came to the point. I was too frightened or something
to enjoy anything."

Analyst: "If there's a crocodile in the cavern its
frightening enough to try it with your toe leave alone with
the feeler of your heart. And here we seem to be proposing
that you do much more than that, in fact, that you dive
in head first with no reserve.

"Why you have been telling me the whole session that
you can't even do that with me, under the protection of
analysis; how can you be expected to dive into Phyllis,

into the cavern, head first with no reserve—and a crocodile inside?

"Earlier in the analysis you were saying that it was all very well to tell you to have no reserve with me; I might as well tell you to walk off a cliff. Well, it's the same thing; cliff—or cavern with the crocodile inside."

This concluded the session.

It will be seen that it was a conflict between abandonment and resistance. And so the conflict goes on between the positive tendency arising from love—of me (originally of his mother), and the negative tendency originating with fear—of "castration" by the crocodile if he attempts to get happiness for himself.

The struggle goes on.

At the end of the session while the patient was getting ready to depart a brief discussion[1] broke out which may take our interest a little further, though not strictly speaking in an analytical direction. He chose to express his resistances in the form of a criticism of the terminology which I had been using.

He said to me: "You know I am scientifically minded, and I don't think much of the sort of terms you use to describe these processes at work in the mind. Your 'armour plate,' these 'crocodiles' and 'caverns.' Admittedly these were originally mine, but you ought to know a better system, or you oughtn't to use symbols at all, you ought to use proper scientific terms denoting the various formulae at work one with the other."

Analyst: "What terms would you use?"

Patient: "Well, I think I would use the letters of the Greek alphabet. We'd say 'beta' for instance instead of

---

[1] In general discussions are best avoided by the analyst. They are usually an attempt on the part of the patient to draw a red herring across the path of analytical, particularly transference, progress. It is doubtful if any amount of experience and knowledge of a patient justifies an analyst, however cautiously, in venturing to indulge in extra-analytical conversation—even extra-analytically. It is safer to treat *all* material as grist for the analytical mill—and for that only.

'armour plate'; everybody should know what it meant. It would be a new terminology. In the same way every warring element would be expressed by a Greek letter or some algebraical formula. Then perhaps the whole thing could be reduced to a sort of mathematical form. There would be more sense in it than in talking about 'armour plating,' 'crocodiles,' and so on."

Analyst: "Of course even if we used anatomical terms, such as phalluses, wombs, etc., we are still only using symbols, for the real subject under discussion is forces within the mind."

Patient: "Exactly. Why use symbols at all?"

Analyst: "It occurs to me that these symbols, not excluding the ones which your sleeping mind has brought forward (crocodiles and caverns) are things which we are conscious of in the real world around us, things which comprise our conscious ways of thinking; and it occurs to me that perhaps everything of which we are aware and with which we deal in our real, waking conscious life, has its counterpart within our minds otherwise we would not deal with it or know that it existed at all.

"It may be that all this world of existence, in so far as we recognize it at all, is recognizable by us, or is there for us, for no other reason than that it corresponds to symbols, the equivalent of your Greek alphabetical symbols, which already exist in our minds.

"It is a fact that this outer world of things which we recognize is a world which created these patterns within our minds, and it is these patterns within our minds which enable us to recognize their counterpart in the outside world. In other words *the world without and the world within (the mental world) are mirrored reflections of each other*. Whether they are anything more or less than this is a deeply philosophical question. In ordinary metaphysics one asks whether our minds are of such stuff that we only recognize things in the real world which correspond to patterns already existing within our minds, and that anything in the outer world which does not so correspond is not known to exist by us. Therefore the real outer world may be something quite beyond our comprehension."

The patient had initiated this discussion on the door step, because he was in great need for some emotional response from his analyst. Having provided him with this amount of intellectualized gratification, admittedly a questionable analytical procedure, I then interpreted the causes of his having led me into it by saying:

"There now! You've always been wanting daddy to come back and play your games and you've succeeded in pressing me into the desired role! Perhaps that will disarm your resistance?"

Chapter XVII

The Mother-Image

IN DUE COURSE we reached a position in the transference when the patient having, partly at least, dealt with the pattern of his emotional relationship to the father-image there began to emerge into consciousness the pattern of his forgotten emotional relationship to the mother-image.

The nature of the psyche is such that this pattern gradually began to reveal itself first and foremost by a succession of dreams and then by a certain amount of reminiscence produced in Association of Thought to this dream material. At the same time a recognition of the emotional importance of the mother-image and of women to his psycho-sexual requirements was very intensely resisted. *Intellectually* some of it was inescapable.

Space will not permit a recital of this voluminous material. Many excellent dreams and their associations will have to be omitted. But from a wide assortment I feel that we had best have just one of these representative dreams and the thoughts the patient produced in connection with it. We may perhaps summarize this stage of his analysis as that of the emergence of the positive-mother-image relationship.

At this session the patient is in no hurry to tell me what he has dreamt. He minimizes the importance of the very real emotional trend which his unconscious is endeavouring to present in his dream material. He begins his session by saying:

"I think I am never myself. I have a different manner for every sort of person. That is why I keep all my friends apart. I am one sort of person for one friend, and another sort for another friend. I am like a chameleon changing my colour according to what I think will suit the particular persons."

Analyst: "That is a sort of ego-work, the sort of activity

in which you specialize! However, one cannot work throughout the twenty-four hours. When do you relax and become yourself? When do you find yourself?"

Patient: "I suppose you would say I do that only in my dreams. When I am with people I do not find myself at all. I can't imagine what would happen if I found myself among a whole group of all my different friends. I think it would be like the story of the chameleon who was put on a piece of tartan—I would just explode. Each friend seems to me to require a different sort of me, and I give him what he requires."

Analyst: "You exercise your technique in relation to his or her particular psychology."

Patient: "Exactly. Nicely put. I have a technique for each person. I think of a whole succession of them now, father-figures, brother-figures, mother-figures and other women. I am concerned only with the impression that I am making on the other person. Even when I am standing on a railway platform waiting for a train I am concerned as to whether I look as I ought to look for my size, age, and so on.

"It is all part of a much bigger problem, namely, the fact that *I don't know what I want to do or to be*. If I knew what I wanted to do or be, then that would decide how I did it. Not knowing what one wants to do is secondary to not wanting union with a woman. You can't arrange to want such a thing as love for a woman, and if you can't arrange that you can't arrange anything else.

"But to me, of course, it is merely a theory that I must want some woman. It is a theory; emotionally it is meaningless to me. Perhaps its nothing to do with sex, but just some affection I want, or in your crazy way of talking you might even say that its the *smell* of my mother or something ridiculous like that.

"How on earth am I to know what I want? There is no guide."

Whatever the patient says even as, or perhaps *especially* as, a joke or a jibe is worthy of analytical note. It seems that the meaning of the paradox "Many a true word is spoken in jest" is this: thoughts or ideas which contain a specially strong unconscious emotional charge, and which are in consequence especially resisted and repressed can only obtain their expression provided their emotional importance is at the same time minimized or denied. Thus the jest or jibe succeeds in expressing them because at the same time it expresses the resistance to them in the form of ridicule.

Thus the fact that the patient mentions "smell" of his mother as an analytical jibe should be duly noted.

To his protest that there was no guide to what he wanted the analyst replied:

"There the dreams will help us because the dreams will tell us what you want."

Patient: "Well, if you must have it here's what I dreamt last night.

"I dreamt I was trying to find a house or a flat and I am trying to find it at a seaside place near Lancaster. I don't seem to be meeting with much success. Then some man directs me in a direction that I hadn't thought of looking in. I go past a garage full of motor cars. I go quite a little way. But I don't find the house. I find a cinema instead. I go inside. Then I find that it's half cinema and half a swimming bath, but the swimming bath part is boarded over and the water keeps coming up through the boards."

For those who like to study how true, how perfect, are the workings of the unconscious mind and how fascinating the revelations of Free Association of Thought, few better examples could be given than the analysis of this little dream and the patient's remarks concerning it.

"The place near Lancaster is the place where I was born and where I lived the first several years of my life with mother and father until I went to a boarding school. That was some time after. I suppose trying to find a house there suggests that I am trying to find our old house, to get back to the situation with mother and father."

Analyst: "To get back to a re-experiencing of the relatively full emotional life which you were then enjoying with mother and father in that house."

Patient: "I think chiefly of the years after my father was dead when I lived there alone with mother. By Jove! It seems that that is what I want to get back to, and yet I've always thought that my one idea was to get away from mother so as not to become like one of these blessed contemptible mother-fixated men. It looks as though you are going to tell me that my real wish, what I really want, is to get back to mother.

"The man I met who directed me in a direction I hadn't thought of must be you. I think now that I was looking for a flat and the man suggested a house, that I should go to a house. Well, of course, the original house: that is mother.

"Anyhow, the man suggested something different, in a direction I hadn't thought of looking. Of course, whether it was you or not I don't know, but this analysis seems to have suggested to me that I ought to be looking for a person in the image of mother, another woman, a wife. That is what seems to me, or rather seems to my feelings, so odd. I hadn't thought of looking in that direction."

Analyst: "What the matter is with you is that it's the old house and the old mother. Your want has not changed in form, that's the trouble. You couldn't return and re-live the emotional patterns of that time of your infancy, so you gave it up. You gave it up consciously, but unconsciously, as your dreams show, you are just the same little boy."

Patient: "When I had it in infancy, it wasn't a want. It's only a want when I'm deprived of it. In trying to follow the direction the man indicated, the direction analysis indicated, I do not seem to find the house at all. I go past a garage full of motor cars, panic stricken. My attachment to you, my preference for men, *à la* father, occurs to me here. Anyhow I passed that."

It is well known to psycho-analysts that motor cars are phallic symbols (i.e. males). A garage is a typical "womb" symbol. Together they symbolize the emotional life which he finally experienced in his maturing relationship to father and mother. The prospect does not gratify him; he is left out. Finally it frightens him, and he passes on, looking for the house or emotional enjoyment of mother prior to this concept of her "occupation" by father. The abundance of cars may be an emphasis of mother's *total* "occupation."

The patient continued: "I don't find the house (the mother). Instead I find a cinema. A cinema is a make-believe, a sham.

"It's all these blessed women I meet, more particularly since I started analysis. To the ego they are potential wives, but my id, my emotional self, is not taken in by that. To it they are just pretending—pretending to be mothers, which they are not.

"Nevertheless, as with a cinema there is some pleasure there; about the same amount of pleasure as one would get in a cinema! But when I go inside its half a swimming bath. I enjoy swimming.

"The swimming bath part is, of course, the sexual part, boarded over so far as I am concerned, while the water keeps coming up. Haven't I told you that women are wet, a nuisance rather than a pleasure? I don't want them, with all their frustrations and difficulties.

"My object in the dream is to find the house at the seaside place. I would rather have the sea than this make-believe swimming bath. The sea is big and worth while. Oh, I suppose you'll say it's mother again, and that's unobtainable. I can't be a baby in a cot all my life, so I don't know what I want. It's all absolutely hopeless."

Analyst: "It occurs to me that most people find their desires, reinforced by sexuality, too good to abandon and they therefore change their form, that is to say change the object of their desires while clinging to the good desires. But you, on the contrary, have clung to the original form of the desires. And as you cannot gratify them in that form, that is to say with mother, you have found your desires and wants no good. As a result you have abandoned them and repressed them and in consequence you don't know what you want."

Patient: "I have observed those men who stick to their mothers, and I have observed those men who want these silly women. They all look so awful that I don't want to look like one of them. I was far too concerned with what people would think of me. Perhaps my weak point is that I allowed public opinion to force me away from mother."

Analyst: "So what you wanted more than anything else was public opinion?"

Patient: "Yes, which must have had its origin in what the parent thought of me. I wasn't sure whether it was my father or my mother that I wanted, but I do know, I am sure, that I did not want to leave home. It is home, more than my parents, that I want. It occurs to me that home represents the interior of mother; the first home, the womb, that is the best.

"I have never been really happy since I came out of it, and this analysis seems to be showing me that I have been trying to get back to it ever since except when I have given up that quest—and then everything is hopeless; I don't know what I want, all I know is that life seems to be quite pointless.

"I am an exile, a blessed exile from my original home near Lancaster, and, like an exile, I am wandering through life without any real incentive to live.

"Being exiled has taken the guts out of life. All I can think of doing is seeing that I cut a good figure instead. But now I think that this exile business started even before childhood. I must have been happy only in the womb, because I can't remember that I was ever very fond of home. Indeed, I remember now that at the age of three I

M

tried to run away from home. I ran as far as my legs would carry me."

A few sessions later there was a particularly interesting corollary to this Association of Thought. The patient came to his session bursting to tell me about it. It had made a profound impression on him.

He said: "I was having an amusing evening with Gladys and her middle-aged man friend. The three of us went off to a night club. I had the first dance with her and he had the second. While they were dancing I got the feeling that I wanted to go away for a walk and before I fully realized what I was doing I found myself walking away from the place.

"It wasn't until I had gone a considerable distance, nearly a mile I should think, that I suddenly realized that I was doing exactly what I had done before at three years of age . . . and for the identical reason.

"I had had no idea of the reason for my walk when I set out. For once I had just followed my impulse instead of my ego. It was just that I had found the situation of sitting there while they danced quite intolerable, just like I felt at the age of three when I found my father's and mother's mutual sufficiency quite intolerable. So I strode away from the place."

It is an analytical speculation that at this time, three years of age, the patient, owing to the growing genital organization of his libido, first sensed the intimacy between his father and mother, and could not stand it, or his exclusion from it. This dancing together of his woman friend, Gladys, and her older partner evidently symbolized this early intolerable scene of sexual union and unconsciously stimulated the reactions which he had first experienced at three years of age. The old emotional pattern is still there.

The patient continued: "When I did realize it, it came to me so vividly that I don't think I ever wanted to go back again; but I turned back. One can't just follow the id all the time. All the way back I experienced a sense of growing depression, something like I generally feel in life. The thought occurred to me 'Oh, my God! I won't be able to say why I walked away.'

"I also had the feeling of the little boy going back to his parents, the feeling of the inarticulateness of the little boy of three years of age. What could he say? He wanted his mummy badly, and he couldn't have her. So the emptiness of the open road was better than the exasperation of being within the smell of mummy and not being able to have her.

"I felt the little boy going back must have felt he was going back to something absolutely terrible because he was so inarticulate. Of course, you couldn't say what you wanted; they wouldn't understand, they couldn't understand. It was worse than going back to prison because it was a prison in which you were not allowed to have the one person you wanted; you were the odd man out, and they were oblivious of it.

"Those are the little boy's feelings. A phrase of Mrs. B's occurs to me. She once said of a little boy 'That little boy enjoys his mummy so much.' I want my mummy. I must have my mummy. It was that man, Gladys's boy friend, who was there taking my mummy away. But to tell you the truth, I like this man very much, but then of course I liked my father very much.

"When I awoke this morning I felt I didn't like Gladys. I felt my attraction towards her had gone. I felt 'I'm clear of that.' And then there came upon me again the emptiness of life—the principal symptom that has brought me to analysis.

"I don't think I've ever seen anything in analysis more clearly than I see this mother-father-me pattern being repeated with Gladys. One of the most interesting things was the feeling that I woke up with, the feeling that I had got Gladys out of my system."

Analyst: "Do you mean that you got your emotional pattern in relation to Gladys out of your system, or do you mean that you got your 'mother-father-me' pattern out of your system?"

Patient: "I meant the former. The latter, the mother-father-me pattern, I thought I had got that out of my system a long time ago, though apparently I have not, as I see from its repetition with Gladys. But in a sense I have, and it was the getting of it out of my system that resulted in this state of depression that I have been in all my life, because it has left me with no alternative pattern, with no emotional point in life, unless of course one can say it was this father-me pattern which has been the cause of my coming to you and the cause of my attachment to you, but that too has gone, or is largely going—another illusion shattered!

"I suppose at the end of all this I'll have even less in life than before, though what I had before was hardly worth having. My last state will be worse than my first. I walked out on them. I'll be walking out on you one of these days. I don't think I've got much confidence left in you as it is. Just give it a little longer, and then . . . .

"Half of me seems to say that it is essential to have complete confidence and to let it rip. I ought not to mind letting myself go, letting it all out. But something in me does mind, something in me walks out on you as it walked out on Gladys and on mother before that. I don't take you completely into my confidence."

Analyst: "This is right at the nucleus of your trouble. Change the word 'confidence' into 'love' and you have it."

Patient: "I can't bring myself to be completely myself with you. I've got nearer to it with you than with anyone else, but the hard core of resistance remains. I was let down by my mother and it seems I am suspicious of being let down by everybody else."

Analyst: "When we've analysed away what causes this resistance you are cured."

Patient: "I think you're right because then there would be no holding back. I would be able to like people. Then I'd be able to love people. Then I would be able to like doing things and I would know what I liked doing. My present position is this eternal suspicion and restlessness and censorship. At present I don't ever want to co-operate with you any more. I would enjoy opposing you except that I'd feel it might be cutting off my nose to spite my face. It seems that I now come here with a sullen opposition."

After a prolonged silence the patient said:
"I think this is a most unpleasant process." His voice had changed and it sounded as though he was almost in tears.

Presently he added: "I'm not going to give way to you. I shan't!"

During the succeeding silence he pulled himself together. Presently he said: "You don't respond. Once upon a time I turned to my mamma and she did not respond. That reminds me that some little time ago I accused Gladys of not responding, of not really falling in love with me. She laughed and replied 'It would be cataclysmic if I did.' What she means is that she dare make superficial responses only, nice and sweet."

Analyst: "Is it the cataclysm in life that you are shunning?"

Patient: "Yes, and so is Gladys. For my part I can tell you here and now that there will be no cataclysm in my life."

Analyst: "What you mean is that there will be no life in your life. You have suffocated it, that is why you are miserable. You have tried to substitute the ego, and the ego is sterile. You can find no real purpose for living. It seems that life, real life, *is* a cataclysm!"

It appears that the patient's dream with which we opened this chapter, and his Associations of Thought to it have uncovered among other things the emotional experiences which led him to run away from his mother and father at the age of three.

It seems also that on account of the mother's failure to respond to his emotional need she became in his mind, as it were, if not a hundred per cent bad object, at least not a hundred per cent good object. There was so much bad mixed up with this good that his immediate reaction was to run away from the object of it just as he ran away from Gladys at the dance.

What he was running away from was, of course, his unpleasant emotional reaction to the mother-father situation. One runs away from unpleasant feelings, but is attracted by pleasant ones. Unpleasant feelings create in the mind "bad objects" as the cause of them. Bad objects are hated and hate causes resistance; one cannot surrender to a bad object.

This was the source of his resistance to his analyst, his resistance to analysis in general, his resistance to his own emotional relief, the cataclysm, or psycho-sexual orgasm, his resistance to emotional life as a whole; you might almost say his resistance to life in general as far as emotions are concerned.

Thus he was reduced to living his life as far as possible purely on an ego plane without emotion, without enthusiasm, without zest and joy. The result must inevitably be sterility, sterility of life both individual and biological, for in such an emotional state, or rather in such an absence of emotional state, a person is unlikely to marry and to propagate his kind. Life is not yet quite dead, but it is rapidly dying out.

As a sequel to this emotional pattern, and in keeping with it, it seems that analysis will be likely to die out. The analyst should take heed. He has been warned. But the dying out of analysis threatens to become not so much a dying out as itself a crisis, a cataclysm, an emergency that calls for all the analyst's resources.

If he, the analyst, were successful this patient might yet be analysed. If he failed it would be the end of analysis, in keeping with the premature termination of this patient's early emotional life.

. It will presently be seen that before we had embarked very far, perhaps not far enough, on the project of overcoming his resistances and uncovering his primitive mother-relationship and his current emotional searching of an unconscious nature, before we had embarked very far on this journey an entirely new situation suddenly arose which threatened to cut across the carefully laid plans of mice and men and to bring his analysis to a premature conclusion.

We shall face this crisis in the next chapter.

BOOK THREE
SON
Transference Proper

Chapter XVIII

The Climax

WE HAVE SEEN how the patient's dream and associated material led to the uncovering of very early memories, of their associated emotional patterns, and of the direct reference of these patterns to his emotional reactions of the present day, to all persons around him, men, women —and particularly towards his analyst. Under cover of his more obvious emotional relationship to males we have revealed to some extent his emotional attitude towards females, and his early infantile pattern in relation to his mother.

At that stage of analysis this sort of material accumulated until it reached voluminous dimensions. The uncovering of infantile memories, *emotionally still active in his everyday life*, continued apace, and the sessions became consequently more and more interesting. In the last chapter we showed an instance of this process at work.

Nevertheless, we shall have to leave the recital of this material, however interesting, as space will not admit its complete exposition. We shall now have to introduce the reader to what may be called the second stage of analysis.

I need make no apology for this abrupt departure because this patient, as is so often the case in analysis, himself introduced the change with even greater abruptness.

As regards the cure of his mental condition, we have so far accumulated only the material for it. It is useful because it will provide the analyst with the necessary armoury upon which he can draw if and when required; but the point about analysis is this: *the real therapeutic changes are emotional changes, not ego changes, and many of these emotional changes still remain to be achieved.*

It is as though we had mobilized our armed forces and amassed their munitions and supplies, but the battle, the emotional battle, has not yet reached its crisis. But we have prepared the equipment for it.

At the next session the patient launched this battle. It will be seen that we were not armed in vain. Almost every resource of the analyst had to be brought into the fight—gradually and without anxiety—to avoid defeat.

It will be seen that we were not unprepared for what happened. It had been showing signs that it must come sooner or later. Several weeks ago a faint cloud no bigger than a man's hand had appeared upon the horizon. It was revealed for instance in the dream where the patient said "the lecturer was no good, and did not even notice what was going on in the classroom." But since then thunderclouds had been gathering for a considerable time, and now at last the storm broke.

This was climax. That it should come, as is often the case, at a time when we were making all these discoveries and might be beguiled into a sense of false security is just typical of the id. It breaks roughshod across all the ego's constructions.

The patient did not smile when I collected him from the waiting room. He barely glanced at me. I observed that his eyes were slightly red-rimmed, and that his face was sullen. He flung himself on the settee and remained silent for a good five or ten minutes. I was about to inquire into the content of his mind when he anticipated me.

He said: "I find it rather depressing to come here." Then, after a short silence—"It would be more sensible to give it up."

There was a protracted silence after this remark, and then he burst out with: "I'm not really telling you the truth. The truth is that I have decided not to come again. This is my last session."

To keep him expressing himself I presently asked: "Why?"

He said: "I feel out of harmony here. I have no confidence in you. I don't trust you. I don't like you. This treatment is getting me nowhere. It is just a useless fraud. All it has succeeded in doing to me is in making me more and more depressed. Anyhow, I'm not going to be a mutt any longer. I nearly didn't come today. But the ego, which you despise and which you have to thank for my present attendance, said to me, 'It is only polite to come just once and tell him that I'm having no more of this nonsense. This is my last session.' "

Pause.

"And now that I've said my say I'm not going to talk any more. I shall just lie here till the time is up and then I'll go and I'll never see your blasted face again. If you want to know the reason, the reason is this: 'that this whole treatment is absolutely useless. It has got me nowhere. It is getting me nowhere, and I can see now that it will never get me anywhere.' So I'm off."

It has often been said that there are two psyches involved in the analytical situation. One is the patient's and the other the analyst's. Of the two the psychology of the analyst is possibly the more important for the achievement of a successful analysis.

Let me for the benefit of the reader for a moment turn my attention to myself and examine my own reactions to this patient's recent remarks. There are several possible reactions. After all, I had spent many months, many daily hours of patient and painstaking inquiry into this patient's psychology. I had listened and suffered all.

In the circumstances it would be only human to react to his remarks as to a slap in the face, and, having got up bruised and battered from the blow, to consider whether it might not be that the patient was right after all, that analysis was perhaps no good, useless, could not achieve any result, and that in devoting so much of my time and of the patient's time to it and in receiving his fees I was, however unwittingly, nothing more or less than a fraud.

Be this so or not, it would still be only human to assume that the patient must be right as regards his own particular case. He had tried so hard, and this was the result. The patient was convinced that he would never get anywhere; the whole treatment was utterly useless.

Did such thoughts as these cross my mind in response to the patient's remarks? I can truthfully tell the reader that I was fully preoccupied with another line of thought altogether. It was something like this:

"It has come . . . the opening of the second stage of this patient's analysis. This is the crisis, the climax. At last he is giving battle. *At last he has brought his emotional life into the analysis.* His gloves are off. His veneer is off. Far from this being the end of analysis, it is the beginning. Emotional analysis which we want, which we must have, is now about to begin."

When I say the gloves are off I do not mean that it was now time for the analyst to sail in and roundly admonish the patient for an ungrateful, aggressive and hostile attitude. Nor even to cross swords with him on an intellectual or ego plane. And least of all to appeal to his emotions and try to wheedle him into a better and more sympathetic emotional attitude. Nothing of the sort.

To achieve success the analyst must above all be an analyst. That is to say, he must know positively that all human emotional reactions, all human judgments and even reason itself, are but the tools of the unconscious; that such seemingly acute convictions which an intelligent person like this possesses are but the inevitable effect of causes which lie buried within the unconscious levels of his psyche.

The analyst must not be concerned with reacting emotionally himself. On the contrary he is concerned solely in investigating, in bringing up to consciousness, the deep-seated causes responsible not only for the patient's emotions, but even for his reason and judgment. The analyst must have had enough experience to know that a cause, an unconscious cause, lies behind all these conscious manifestations. He must never be beguiled into accepting them on their reality appearances.

With this in mind I took the first opportunity of asking the patient to do Free Association of Thought to the feelings of depression and anger which he was experiencing.

He said: "The uselessness of it all . . . the pointlessness of it all . . . the pointlessness of life."

I was then able to remind him that it was just this pointlessness of life which had led him to seek analysis. This had now crept into the analysis itself. The burning question was what was the primary source of these feelings of hopelessness which originally had caused him to present himself for analysis, and which now made the analysis itself seem hopeless.

The answer to this all-important question was not immediately forthcoming. When it does emerge you will see the wisdom of clinging to the analytical rather than to the rational method. No amount of reasoning would ever have revealed anything so ridiculous as the source of his hopelessness eventually proved to be, ridiculous on the reasoning plane, but nevertheless the very essence of all his hostile reactions to me and to the analysis, and particularly the foundation of his state of depression.

Presently I was able to point out to him that some change was evident. I said: "*You are feeling something more than you used to feel.*"

He said: "I certainly am. I feel I would like to sock you on the jaw!" (He shakes his fist in the air.)

Then, more quietly: "I realize that I'm implicating myself in saying that. I'm revealing how bothered I am . . . that I have so much feeling about it."

After a brief silence he continued: "If you can't make a person react emotionally to you, if you can't and realize you can't, the only thing is to get away from him and prevent yourself from continuing to be disturbed. If you don't get away from him then there's nothing else to do except to hit the person in the end, or kick him or punch him. No other way of showing your feelings."

Analyst: "And at the same time *forcing* me to feel something with you after all . . . and something not only emotional but also physical—in short, orgastic!"

Patient: "At last it seems that I have direct knowledge of an instinct want: to force you to do something with me. And, if you won't, to sock you."

Analyst: "What did you want with your daddy?"

Patient: "I wanted to get into bed with him and be tickled. But he did not frustrate me like you do. I frequently got into bed with him and got tickled until I was hysterical . . . a bit frightened at the same time, but what a thrill!"

Analyst: "And what did you anticipate from me?"

Patient: "Good God! Do you mean it's the same thing? Do you mean that for all these months I've been coming here it has not been in the hope of solving my intellectual problem or acquiring insight, but simply in the hope that you would do something, the same as my father did, take me into bed with you and tickle me until I lost all control? Good Lord! I believe it is. How positively ridiculous."

Here we have the answer to the question which occurred a little earlier in the chapter. What *was* this patient unconsciously expecting from analysis, the frustration of which made it seem so hopeless?

He continued: "Still my father did not frustrate me. He did rough and tumble with me. You are as blasted cold and unsatisfactory as an iceberg."

Patient reflecting: "After all my father did not live after I had approached puberty. I wonder what I'd have wanted or expected from him if he had gone on living. Tickling would hardly have been enough at fifteen. I suppose I would have given him up in favour of something else, a girl perhaps. But he had already died so I did not have to give him up.

"I came to you to work it all out with you . . . on you . . . or perhaps under you. Something in me does feel it would be nice to have an intimate relationship with you, but of course my ego realizes that that would not solve my problems. Still I feel a grievance because I do not see the necessity of the frustration . . . that the frustration should come from you."

After a silence: "Anyhow, it seems that the rage with you is over. I suppose I was impotent in my childhood and I'm impotent to give it full expression now. That's why it's over. I have given it up. That's why I want to go from analysis . . . to give it all up . . . to give you up."

Analyst: "Had your father lived he would have similarly frustrated you and you would have given up your emotional fixation to him in the same way and for the same reasons as you are giving up your attachment to me. The pity is that owing to his death you were able to maintain and develop your libidinal relationship to him in phantasy. That is how you remained father-fixated; there was nothing, no reality, to discount the fixation. In connection with me you unconsciously sought to actualize this phantasy. It is now being frustrated and is in consequence disintegrating. First you want to hit me for frustrating you. That is inhibited and so you feel impotent. Next you try to repress the feelings and claim that you do not feel anything at all. That has been your main defence throughout life. But the very intensity of your emotion in giving me up belies the pretence. What are the feelings which you are trying to conceal?"

Patient: "It's the eternal frustration that is so exasperating."

Analyst: "What was the stage in your life when you felt that?"

Patient: "Childhood."

Analyst: "So finally you chuck it up."

Patient: "Yes. It's an emotional situation and I walk out on it, which reminds me that I walked out on Gladys at the dance the other day. It is frustration which leads one to repress and repudiate all one's emotional desires like I have done. The frustration is the failure to get you

N

to react emotionally to my feelings. I suppose I have unconsciously tried to make you a good-object and you haven't played, and in the end I've felt hopelessly frustrated and so rejected you. I had to reject you. At first, during the happy days of these sessions, you must have stood for expected or hoped-for gratification. Now you stand only for frustration.

"It's only when I'm unpleasant to you that I realize how little you have ever responded. To you I am simply a patient going through a process which he only dimly understands. That is the frustrating element. You have no idea how frustrating that is. It's so frustrating to think that there is nothing pleasant in the relationship. That is why I feel you are no use to me."

Analyst: "You have been through all these phases before, when you were a child. There is a first phase of increasing expectation mounting to excitement. On a sexual analogy we would call it tumescence. Firstly, you are confidently expecting, anticipating, some emotional, perhaps physical, relationship with the parent.

"This hope grows to a certain pitch, and then when it does not achieve gratification or adequate gratification it has to be bolstered up as it were. You go on with it hoping against hope. Gradually it becomes difficult to keep up this hope in the face of no adequate gratification.

"Then finally, particularly at five and again at puberty you struggle to maintain it in phantasy. It is only finally given up at twenty-nine with me. The good-object is revealed as not good. The good-object is that which gratifies. From being not good this object finally becomes bad, a frustration. And what do we do with bad-objects, whether they are material in the stomach, or not-gratifying or hurtful mental material? We reject them. We vomit them up. We refuse to ingest any more such stuff. We withdraw from the frustrators in our life. We turn them out, withdraw into ourselves, achieve a position of isolation, protection against any emotional impingement of persons outside ourselves. But this state is an attempted reconciliation to disappointment, the abandonment of gratification, the repudiation of the once hoped-for happiness. In short, it is Depression.

"On a sexual analogy we might say: detumescence without adequate orgasm equals depression."

Patient: "I had already given it up with mother before I tried it out with father, and now after all these years I've tried it out again on you."

It should be obvious to the reader that the material of this session here detailed is of the utmost importance. Not only is the material important, but of special practical, technical importance is the conducting of a session which begins in the way that this session began.

The all-important matter is not to accept the patient's material on the reality plane, not to react emotionally to it, but to recognize that this is an emotional situation in the patient's mind calling for an analytical, unemotional attitude on the part of the analyst.

The analyst's business is to find what lies underneath all this, irrespective of whether the material is hate or love, or just ideas, ego-material, opinions, dispassionate judgment or a dream. They are all grist for the analytical mill; and, this is the important thing, they are all without exception nothing more or less than this.

By recognizing this fact at the outset and by persisting in the analytical technique we have turned threatened failure into possible success. The patient has achieved a deeper and truer recognition of his early and current emotional pattern than he had previously achieved. No doubt this situation will not be final, these battles will probably all have to be fought over again, and repetitively, but every victory gained, and this is an important victory, will add up until the domination of these blind, semi-unconscious emotional patterns over the patient's reasoning life will be undermined and finally destroyed.

Only then will the field be clear for the formation of newer and better patterns. Or, if he is too old for this last event to take place, at least his psyche will be rid of an unnecessary emcumbrance, an encumbrance which might have thwarted his ego-adjustment to the realities of life. Already his past patterns are beginning to have less domination over his conduct in life.

He says: "Always I have been attracted to the man, but always finally the man has become a frustration and a source of depression to me because one cannot have physical relationship with a man. The woman, on the other hand, is meaningless from a mental point of view. There is no real mental attraction or attachment to her. I am able to use her physically, but what is the good of that when the real attraction is towards the man?

"It has been on this account that in my adult life the nearest I could get to complete satisfaction was to get mental union with the man and to have intimacy with his wife physically, and that is what has actually happened on many occasions, and it's usually the wife of my best friend. What a social menace I have been! The odd part about it is that it has never been for the wife's sake, but for the man's sake."

I here remind him that at one very enthusiastic stage of his analysis he had a fairly protracted bout of promiscuity.

To this he remarks: "But the excitement was not what I did with girls, the excitement was to come here and tell *you* all about it. That's what I was looking forward to. I suppose I was having a sort of intimacy with you by proxy. Throughout my life my only alternative to this sort of emotional muddle has been to crush all my emotions— that is what I have generally done—and to substitute in their place a programme of ego-activity.

"I mapped out the whole of my life. I made it all a task. I saw to it that I wasn't lazy. I found something according to my programme of ego-activity that I must be doing almost every moment of the day. Good gracious, what pitiful uphill work it was! Do you know, the curious thing is that now I don't mind being lazy. While I did all these things on an ego plane, deep down I was still the victim of this daddy attachment. I was still daddy's little boy, miserable without a daddy.

"What nonsense I talked about running away from analysis. I am inescapably in this analysis, just as inescapably as one is one's father's son."

Nevertheless, the patient's increasing insight into all this was beginning to make some changes. He says:

"Do you know at twelve or earlier I think I must have been assuming, though unconsciously, what fun daddy would be when I became a little more sexually mature."

Analyst: "And later you tried to make your dreams come true with me as a reality equivalent of the father-image, only to come upon an insuperable obstacle. To quote your own phrase, 'it doesn't get us anywhere.' And then you regressed back to Sundays in bed, back to phantasy and masturbation."

Patient: "Do you know in my early masturbation phantasies I believe it was father involved."

Analyst: "What role did he play?"

Patient: "Obviously he would do it to me, like he tickled, he would make me have feelings, orgasm."

Analyst: "And now what was your rage with me about?"

Patient: "Oh, obviously you wouldn't do anything. I could only have made you feel anything by hitting you."

Analyst reflecting: "Is that what fights between males are all about, not excepting wars? Has all your depression been because I would not play?"

Patient: "Yes, in spite of all we say, I still feel it like that. In a way I might say I feel worse because I realize now that I've lost the possibility of ever finding a father."

This deep-seated realization was a change, or heralded a change, an improvement. Ego changes are one thing, but id changes, *or rather changes in the repressed unconscious phantasies*, are infinitely more difficult to achieve and it is *these latter* that count. *They* are already taking place.

When I had occasion to say to him: "Your emotional pattern is the child-father pattern," he replied, with some conviction: "It *was*, but it is not any longer. I'm not interested in fathers any longer. If I stop analysis I go out into a wintry world where all fathers have been destroyed. Your only value to me is that you represent the last vestige of the father-figure, and without you I really would have to stand on my own feet emotionally. After a slight pause he added: "I almost feel I could now."

This heralds the cure of his compulsive subservence to the unconscious phantasy of union with the father-image, and opens the possibility for the first time of the patient himself becoming a father—a father in the social sense of the word, as well as in the biological sense.

Chapter XIX

He has Prospects of Inheriting the Mother-Image

THE PATTERN of this patient's emotional relationship to his father has been re-experienced within his analytical sessions using the analyst as the new object or father-image in this relationship. He has passed through the whole gamut of this relationship from the time when he played trains, from the time when he sobbed and, most vividly, to the time when he encountered frustration of his whole object-libido and experienced his repressed hate impulses. He has seen that his unconscious expectations of gratification with this father-image were responsible for his initial enthusiasms, and, recognizing this, he has seen further that there is no hope in reality even on a merely mental plane of consummating this infantile love affair. The truth has been painfully borne home to him. Despite all resistance on the part of the pleasure-principle he has at last been forced to accept the facts. With this acceptance there is an immediate deep-seated recognition, particularly on an emotional plane, that the entire situation is utterly "useless." That is why he has said "Analysis is no good. There is no point in my coming any more."

However, the interpretation of the cause of these feelings of his towards analysis in general and his analyst in particular had the effect of making him desire further insight; and so without any direct appeal to his reasoning, or, in other words, without persuasion, the patient himself insisted upon going on with his attendance. He felt, and rightly, that he must know more about this.

The analyst was at this stage of the proceedings due to take a few weeks' holiday, but with proper understanding of the situation he could do so without any anxiety regarding its effects upon the continuation of treatment.

On the resumption of analysis the patient began his session at rather an ego level by a recapitulation of what

he had learnt from his recent analytical experiences. Perhaps this recapitulation will not be amiss for the reader
also.

He said: "I can see the outline of my entire emotional
development. It was like this: originally I wanted my
mother, but having lost her I turned to father as a secondary. So I made a friend of father instead of an enemy of
him, but thereby I lost mother completely. Father is not
a bad substitute when one is a little boy. Perhaps he
would have become a bad substitute if he had remained
alive, but he died.

"Before puberty I was yearning for him. Any heterosexual feelings that I may have had had become buried
under that father-yearning. It was through this that I
established an emotional pattern, or at any rate included
an object (father) as an essential of that emotional pattern,
which was impracticable and left me no way out at all.
The result was that I would always remember the fun of
being with daddy. There was indeed a conscious memory
of *niceness* with daddy, but, and this is my tragedy, there
was no sort of memory of any niceness with mother. The
consequence was that, quite naturally, I was always
looking for father-figures or persons in the image of daddy
with whom to experience that niceness, the only niceness
which I could remember, all over again. In this way it
would not occur to me naturally to look for any niceness
with a person in female form."

Perhaps to provoke him I remarked: "If you could feel
the same *daddy*-way towards a woman then there would
be a solution?"

He said, tersely, "Of course, but I just can't! In fact the
contrary is the case. I have been at several parties with
many so-called attractive women, but they have not
registered with me in the slightest degree. I am just not
interested.

"As a matter of fact that is an exaggeration. I was
not interested several months ago, but since these recent
sessions with you and during your holiday I found to my

surprise that I was a little interested, more interested than I have ever been before. But it is not much. Even while with the women I was thinking rather of resuming my sessions with you."

Analyst: "You are a sick boy suffering from homesickness. In a state of homesickness one is not interested in the persons around one. One only wishes to be home. With me you are home again."

Patient: "Yes, I realized that at the time. That reminds me that I was with my mother at the beginning of the holidays and I did not let myself go with her. Almost purposely I found her dull and boring. There was no question of being in tune with her, simply because I just was not broadcasting."

Analyst: "It is interesting to note that you found it necessary to put up a defence against the possibility of emotional relationship to your mother. At the same time it seems you were sickening for me."

Patient: "Quite. And during the fortnight's holiday I wanted to come back to you, but I felt cut off from you. That is why I have not felt much better, and now I am here with you I still feel cut off. That seems to be my trouble now."

Analyst: "It seems that your happiness depends upon your emotional entanglement with me."

Patient: "My trouble is that it is no longer a satisfactory emotional entanglement. It is a one-sided affair. *I must admit that your attitude to me has been consistent throughout; therefore if this entanglement has changed it must be because I have changed.*"

Analyst: "What changes have taken place, and why?"

No answer.

Analyst: "There have been these ideas of breaking off from me. Why?"

Patient: "Because nothing was happening."

Analyst: "You mean your anticipations were not being realized. You were not receiving any gratification."

Patient: "I realize now that I was, as it were, sinking

myself in you. It has taken me a long time to discover that nothing is coming out of that, and so at last I have tried to retain, or to return to, some independent identity, that is to say to emerge from this fusion with you. The independent identity means breaking off from you, going away."

Analyst: "In spite of reality, the draw of the pleasure-principle has been too much for you and you have been enjoying the phantasy of gratification by union with me. Now the illusion is broken and you have been feeling and behaving as though hope were dead and the love affair was at an end."

Patient: "There are two me's. One is the 'me sensible' and the other 'me the ass.' At last 'me sensible' has said to this other chap 'Don't be a fool any longer. Give this fellow up.' But, and this is my tragedy, the only effect of the 'me sensible' is to increase the distress of the situation. 'Me the ass' cannot 'give this fellow up.' It seems it would die."

Analyst: "What is it that you could never give up? What is it that would result in your death if you gave it up?"

Patient: "The wherewithal of life."

Analyst: "What was that in the first instance?"

Patient: "I cannot deduce it logically, but suddenly as you spoke I felt what it was. It was mother's nipple!"

Analyst: "So 'me the ass' must continue to suck mother's nipple for its very life *even though 'me sensible' sees that it is merely a dummy which it is sucking.*"

Patient: "Yes, and I have been doing that for months and am still doing it, although 'me sensible' sees that it is so useless."

Analyst: "What you are seeing now is that if you go over to the sensible side you lose everything—except sense."

Patient: "Sense is so useless, and there is no way out."

Thus as is so often the case in analysis we are brought to a recognition of the fact that life is not a rational process but an emotional one based upon instinct gratification. If "sense" alone prevailed depression would supervene and sooner or later life itself would cease to exist. The biological urge canalized in its instincts is the basis of life, of its continuance as well as of its creation, and sense is merely its servant.

After a pause the patient continued. I had not spoken but apparently the same thought had occurred to him:

"There are two states: The emotional state is happy and senseless, but it is life, baby life, it is babyhood. The sense state is unhappy, sterile and lifeless. It is death, or on the way to it."

Analyst: "Free Association of Thought to this senseless happiness."

Patient: "That is where one person is affected by another emotionally, and both feel it. That is they are rubbing together."

Pause.

"Somehow I thought then of myself as a baby on my mother's breast . . . I believe now that that was the only happy period of my life . . . that was when I was having my gratification . . . and it was obviously with mother. I have a feeling now that my trouble must have started when I was weaned. It must have been too early. Mother had disappointed me. After all one can only be disappointed if one has actually experienced the pleasure of which one is then deprived. In my disappointment I turned to father and I have flogged that hope ever since. I have been flogging it all the time I have been coming to you, having put you in place of the dead father. Now at last I feel that changes have taken place—and I have felt different about life. There is something I have lost, but this difference must be some sort of a gain, and so I think we will try it a bit longer."

Analyst: "We have lost this feeling of anticipation of gratification with the male."

Patient: "Yes, but I don't mind that; that loss is a gain because it was a will o' the wisp anyhow."

Analyst: "Your trouble is that we have found no other means of gratification."

Patient: "So we have got to go back further, and find out how and why I lost my mother."

Analyst: "The answer is *in exactly the same way as you lost me.*"

Here the patient burst into laughter—always a sign that some emotional tension has been released.

"Yes, I lost you, or gave you up, because you would not respond emotionally."

After a pause he added the significant remark "You would not feed me—just as my mother suddenly refused to continue her feeding of me. Apparently I have wanted you to respond in the same way as for a long time I wanted my mother to respond, by putting me to the breast again. If she had done, by Jove! wouldn't I have bitten her! It occurs to me now that I did bite her once or twice for keeping me waiting, for frustrating me. And that was the origin of my hate.[1] When she would not put me to the breast again my hate grew; I suffered, became miserable, as I have done here, and finally I gave her up, left her, as I have recently wanted to leave you. She was no further good to me, merely a source of aggravation and distress, so I left her and I turned to my father. He seemed to fill the gap. At least he did respond. He was delighted to have me. He put me into bed with him, rubbed my cheek and tickled me so that I was at least distracted from what I had previously wanted. I never wanted to look towards my mother again. It was too distressing; and never since have I looked properly towards any person in the image of my mother. Father never gave me the disappointment and the pain which she had given."

[1] We thus see the origin of hate from oral frustration—e.g. through an inadequate supply of milk. No doubt it is later reinforced by anal and genital frustrations.

Analyst: "But your needs were the same, the need for gratification, and all you had done about it was to change the image or object from which you expected the gratification. In other words it was not the pattern, the emotional pattern of need for gratification, which had changed since the days of your attachment to mother, it was merely the smell or object of that gratification which had changed from female to male. Put differently we might say that you were acting out the identical pattern with father that you had previously acted out with mother. Only the object from which you were to get gratification had changed. It was still gratification that you were after. In the same way that you transferred this pattern from mother to father you have, in the course of your analysis, transferred it from father to me.

"We have been saying that I was your father, or father-image, and you were re-enacting your expectation of gratification with your father in this analysis, using me as the object instead of him. Now we can see that it is equally correct to say that I was your mother and that you were expecting to achieve all the gratifications which you had once experienced with mother, and of which she had deprived you, at my hands. Your difficulties have arisen from the fact that mother did two things, one: she gratified you, and two: she subsequently withdrew and refused gratification. Thus from being a source of pleasure she became a source of intolerable distress. Therefore you substituted father for her, and this new object was retained because it had the advantage of never having given you either complete gratification or complete frustration. And so you were still in a position to hope for complete gratification from this new object, a substitute for the original mother-object. Unfortunately for the realization of your emotional requirements the "mother" had by this mechanism taken on the form or appearance of the male, and so in a sense you have gone through life looking for persons in the image of your father, unconsciously hoping that these persons would put you to the breast and gratify that original longing and restore that hope of which mother had deprived you.

"Thus we see that we have arrived at a further stage of analysis for now the mother-object within the emotional pattern is being encountered whereas previously it had not been possible to penetrate to a deeper level than that of the father or male object."

With the uncovering of the underlying mother-object and re-emergence into consciousness of the memories of his mother and the nice feelings he had at her hands as an infant, this patient will become increasingly in a position to seek for his gratifications, oral and otherwise, at the hands of an object in the image of his mother. That is to say he will tend to become more heterosexual. Whereas previously feminine objects were emotionally meaningless to him, as all affects originally pertaining to the mother had been transferred on to the father-image, he is now beginning to recognize, and perhaps even to *feel*, that the hope of gratification, of a solution of the psyche's desires, lies in the direction of women rather than of men.

Chapter XX

Analysis of the Transference

IN OUR LAST two chapters we have shown how at an advanced stage of analysis, with the onset of transference resistance and its interpretation, our patient's ambivalent attachment to the father-image was so considerably weakened that he would cease from everlastingly seeking father-figures as an essential ingredient of his emotional life.

For instance, he said *and felt* "I'm not interested in fathers any longer. If I stop analysis I go out into a wintry world where all fathers have been destroyed. Your only value to me is that you represent the last vestige of the father-figure and without you I really would have to stand on my own feet emotionally. I almost feel I could now."

In this chapter we shall see a little more fully than we saw in the last chapter how the analyst, by virtue of his emotional detachment, can function equally well as a *mother*-image, and have placed upon him the patient's forgotten emotional fixations to the mother of his infancy.

It was the repression of the emotional pattern of this fixation and its rigidity that prevented the patient from re-casting his emotional needs in a normal way, in a way that would attach him mentally to a woman with whom he could at the same time overcome the genital-sexual frustration so inevitable in mother love, and consummate his entire *psycho-sexual* need in a manner both potent (i.e. no longer frustrating) and biologically sound.

I am afraid that the opening of this chapter may not be very interesting to the reader, but I hope his application to it will in the end be amply repaid. Its importance for an understanding of the process of analytical cure cannot be over estimated.

First of all we must go back to the session immediately preceding the one mainly to be described in this chapter —a session which had been unfortunate owing to the absence of my secretary and the intrusion of matters beyond my control.

The patient had lain on the analytical settee motionless and silent.

When after a considerable time I asked him what he was conscious of he replied "I think I am going to sleep."

Analyst: "Would you rather sleep with me here, or alone?"

Patient: "I would rather be alone."

Analyst: "I am wondering whether your answers are true."

Patient: "Well, then, I am deluding myself!"

After a considerable time of this sort of demonstration from the patient, chiefly characterized by persistent silences, he was pressed to do Free Association of Thought to the mood in which he was.

He replied: "Indifference."

Analyst: "Does this mood and attitude bring to your mind any similar experience from childhood?"

Patient: "Yes. Sulks. But there is not the solemn resentment of sulks. In this case it is just indifference."

Analyst: "Sulking is a negation, a denial, and don't you think that this indifference is a further negation of a negation? If sulks equals 'I shan't,' don't you think this indifference might be expressed by the words 'I shan't sulk'?"

At last after half an hour of this battle with the patient's resistances we had evidently hit upon something that loosed his tongue a little.

He said: "In a way one can say indifference is the only weapon to beat you with, the only retaliation I know."

Analyst: "And what have I done that you must beat me?"

Patient: "It is what you have not done. You have done nothing . . . except what you have taken away . . . in the end you have taken *everything* away . . . that is there is nothing left to do, nothing . . . and you might as well see a demonstration of it in here as outside."

Analyst: "That is true if I am the *real* world."

Patient: "Lack of interest in the real world is due to what you have taken away. That is you have exposed the illusions. The things I kept myself going with are exposed as useless. In a way I knew it before, but I know it much more clearly now. You have let me down completely."

Analyst: "If you expected all at my hands and I have remained outside your life, then I have let you down."

Patient: "In any case it would be a let down."

Analyst: "What would *not* be a let down?"

Patient: "I suppose the stock answer is if you gratified all my emotional needs. But I can tell you that if we even lived together and had our emotional lives together it would still be a let down because there would be an inevitable frustration. Something of the sort was present during my childhood and that is why I sulked."

Before the end of this session it transpired that the patient had earlier in the day left a message to the effect that he would not be keeping his appointment for the following day. I asked him why he had done this, and he replied:

"I prefer to go and see Mr. X who is ill in Birmingham."

Mr. X is a subordinate of the patient of whom he had previously remarked to me "They put him on the sick list. The Doctors call it blood pressure, but to my mind it is sex pressure. The silly old buffer has been in the habit of having relations with his wife three times a week and now that her pregnancy is very advanced he does not have it at all, and this physical factor, coupled with his anxiety about his wife's coming confinement, has given him these headaches and landed him in the hands of doctors equally innocent on a mental plane of the existence of sexuality."

I indicated to the patient that the proposed visit to Mr. X, like his pretended indifference during the session, was nothing more or less than a red herring to hide the fact that he was reacting to the negative, or hate, element in his transference by the standard method of absenting himself—in a further attempt to annoy the analyst.

He rudely repudiated this suggestion and said:

"Mr. X it is going to be. Besides, I have already sent him a post-card and could not let him down if I wanted to, which I don't."

The above session was on a Wednesday. On the Friday, when the patient was due for his next session, I received what could only be called a "phoney" letter from him in which he listed in itemized form his complaints about the previous session. It was headed "Record of a fifty-minute session with Dr. Berg, Psychologist.

"6.50 p.m. Session starts, twenty minutes late.

"7.0 p.m. Telephone interruption.

"7.10 p.m. Telephone interruption.

"7.25 p.m. Telephone interruption.

"7.30 p.m. Interruption while next patient is admitted to waiting room.

"7.40 p.m. End of session.

"7.42 p.m. Analyst makes strong suggestion that cancellation of 6.30 session for the following day should be ignored and advanced analytical reasons.

"7.45 p.m. Patient departs poorer by the amount of his fee."

When he arrived that Friday evening he again lay motionless on the analytical settee, but without so prolonged a silence as on the previous occasion.

Presently, he said: "I am glad I did not come yesterday." Then it transpired that he had in the end not been to see Mr. X. He felt he explained this adequately by saying:

"When I got home I found I had forgotten to post his

post-card after all! Anyway, I had an excellent long
evening all by myself."

At this I pointed out to him that he had spent at least
a portion of the evening in spiritual communion with me
as evidenced by his letter posted that evening. He here
expressed surprise that I should refer to his letter as
previous follies of this description had been contemptuously
ignored by me. Asked for an analysis or interpretation of
his conduct he proved a little more co-operative than
previously.

He admitted: "I felt guilty at having cancelled the
appointment with you and I wrote that letter to show
that *you* were guilty because attack is the best form of
defence. By this means I repudiated any guilt which I felt."

I took this opportunity of pointing out to him that at
the session before the Wednesday the time had been
prolonged to over one hour without interruption and he
had made no reference to this, thus showing that a
motive for the material content of his letter was an
expression of the negative or hate element of his transference, and therefore an omission of the other side of the
ambivalence. He corrected me here by saying:

"Ah, but I sent you a cheque as well—posted later I
admit. I suppose you haven't received it yet."

Thus the positive side has also been expressed in the
end.

Presently we penetrated the armour of his assumed
indifference to me and to his analysis and he admitted
that it was after all a form of sulking exactly similar to
that in which he had indulged so much during his infancy
with only this difference: that whereas in infancy he
naïvely displayed his sulkiness, here he tried to deny its
existence by an assumption of indifference. He went on to
explain that sulks were the inevitable, the unalterable,
result of the emotional state which he was in both then
(in infancy) with his mother, and now with me. There
were two explanations of this inevitableness and this
unalterableness.

He said: "Firstly, it is all frustrating. I have no way of showing my love or my feelings. All I can do is to burst into tears and that makes me all the more determined to sulk my way through life. The sulks mean that I am not going to be broken down by a superior emotional attack such as I might get from my mother. The second reason is that mother love was for me at that stage of my life the wrong sort of love. Mother love is no use. I have got to have admiration. It has got to be *a love situation which I can dominate*. In other words, my mother would have to be the willing slave before she could remove the sulks. I go on sulking because by that means (in my infantile mind) I may in the end get a weeping mother subservient to me. My feeling is that in the end I shall dominate her. She will plead for my love . . . that is what I want. But the blessed woman won't do it. Hence I come to the conclusion that I will not give way next time. I will make her beg for my love."

Having completed this rather brilliant sample of memory analysis, the patient says, reflectingly,

"And that brutal pattern has crystallized in my adult life, so that now she does beg for my love and is a darned nuisance."

Presently he goes on to say "I can remember clearly that that is what I wanted when I was sulking. I wanted my mother to become subservient to me . . . to plead for my love. By analogy that is what I am trying to do to you. That is what I wanted you to do last Wednesday . . . I wanted you to beg me to stay, to beg me to come back the following day. And I would not come, so, as I have said, I felt guilty and I wrote that letter to show that you were guilty. It is all most frustating and most unsatisfactory, and I can do nothing about it but sulk or pretend to be indifferent . . . just the same as it was with mother. Like her you could only patronize and that is not gratifying. One cannot respond to patronizing love . . . no response is possible. What is left to the little boy? He might kick her in the shins, but father is in the background to deal with that. If on the other hand she, or you, have lost me emotionally and you have got to beg for me to return emotionally, *then I* can dispense the favours. But now I see that even then it is frustrating, because what can you do about it even then?"

Presently he continues: "If my sulking had caused her to collapse I would have been the first to stage a reconciliation and a very powerful one it would have been, because then I would have been able to dominate and to dispense the favours."

Now we come to the crux of this session. I here pointed out to the patient that with this frustrating emotional tie-up with his mother-image his sexual impulse could not consciously come into the picture, and had to be repressed, but unconsciously it was periodically gaining its pseudo-marital outlet in the form of his occasional masturbatory acts in which, interestingly enough, there was usually no conscious image. He admits that this must be the case.

He said: "You have emotional fun and games with your mother, and you masturbate because you have no means of expressing the emotion. Even the infant-part of me cannot have a sexual relationship with her and therefore I sublimate it all by sending flowers—or in your case cheques—and rude letters. Unless, of course, I can come here and sulk it out.

"Now I recognize that all this is waste of time because the primitive instinct, sex, is frustrated. It is frustrated because it is directed to one's mother, or to you, and so it cannot be gratified."

Analyst: "And so you sulk again—sulk openly, and masturbate secretly."

Patient: "It is the suppliant woman who is the woman you can gratify yourself with sexually. You have got to get your woman in that pliant state before you can dominate her and use her sexually. Therefore all my efforts (sulking) towards mother were an attempt at seduction.

"She, good woman, never let me get her down. She has

said 'You used to get in such tempers, but I knew it was useless to give way to you because that would be spoiling you.' And so I see that it was always frustrated because the sulking tactics never worked. Also it was too painful for me to withdraw my own affections for long enough to make it work."

Analyst: "It is because of the fixation of your emotional life in this pattern that you do not get it out in normal life with its sexual accompaniment."

Patient: "I do the sulking with the present-day young woman too, only I do it on a more civilized plane. I do it, exactly the same thing, by *indifference*. But it is all in a minor key because I know it isn't mother anyway. That is to say, even if I do get her suppliant I know it is not the original mother. On the other hand, if it is mother or too like mother I cannot feel any sexual desire towards her, that is forbidden, and so I am caught either way."

He had found the insight he had gained at yesterday's session so illuminating that he felt a certain conscious or ego satisfaction as a result. But when he lay down on the settee again for this session that feeling vanished and he found himself again experiencing the same frustration with which he had started the previous session. This was a surprise and disappointment to him. At this point I indicated to the patient that insight was never in itself adequate compensation for the failure to gratify an instinct. For example, a person who is suffering from an empty feeling inside may discover that he is hungry. He may even discover why he is hungry, but would it be surprising if he found himself still hungry when he has not had any dinner after all? Analysis is no substitute for life any more than the discovery that one is hungry and why is a substitute for dinner. If one tries to make it a substitute one becomes depressed or ill.

The patient here referred to a dream fragment in which he was sitting in a restaurant when an attractive woman came and sat on one side of him and tried to gain his attention, and then another attractive woman came and seated herself on the other side of him, but, he said characteristically: "I succeeded in remaining indifferent to them both."

I asked him to continue this as a day dream.

He said: "They would try to make themselves more and more attractive in order to break down my indifference, but as they did so I would increase my resistance and succeed in being proof against it all."

He here compares it to the sort of game one plays in childhood. For instance, one challenges the other child that he cannot open one's clenched hand. The harder one's adversary struggles to open one's hand the tighter one clasps it. The fun lies in the contest.

He continued: "It is a silly sort of game. They, the women, try to catch me, but I am too strong. I am proof against it all. Of course, if they don't play that game it is hopeless. The excitement lies in the game."

Analyst: "There we have your emotional life—this game. It is out of this that you are getting your excitement and you have brought it here into your analysis to play it out with me hoping that I will play my role."

Patient: "I admit it. I feel here that I am not going to do anything. I feel that you have got to try and make me. If you don't try there is no game, it is just disappointing. What happens in reality for instance with a woman is that she just gives up playing. I think now of the tickling games of childhood. I would say 'I'm not ticklish. You try me.' And then I would try not to feel anything and the harder the person tried to make me feel ticklish the more I would set myself against feeling it. Of course, adults are so silly that they often said 'Oh, you are not ticklish anyway' and gave it up, and that was most disappointing."

Analyst: "What would you like to happen?"

Patient: "What I would like is to be broken down or over-ruled, or made to feel something against my will. Tickling is very important. In the tickling of children they experience their first breakdown; the burst of laughter is just like the detumescence. I refer to the *initial* breakdown into laughter. Now in later life I am offering a challenge to every woman. The challenge amounts to this: 'You cannot tickle my feelings, I am not ticklish.' If only one of them would succeed she might find out how ticklish I am and how much I want to be tickled. But I think the strength of my resistance is principally due to the fact that if she did succeed then she would remain a dominating figure, a mother-figure, not the suppliant figure that a woman tends to become when she gets going. The sulks or indifference is really an attempt to reverse the roles. If I could remain indifferent, then I would be successful, or that is the illusion I nurse."

Analyst: "What would be satisfactory?"

Patient: "Nothing, because if they succeed I am not dominant, I am only a happy loser. It is not really satisfactory if the other boy does succeed in forcing your hand open."

Analyst: "What would be satisfactory?"

Patient: "I don't know. You see my whole life is built up of this resistance principally. All I can think of saying is that provided the other party enters into the struggle, resistance is satisfactory . . . but it is not really because it leads to strangulation. The only solution would be to throw all this pattern overboard and start out again."

Analyst: "Is there no alternative to the incompletely satisfactory result of your being the happy loser?"

Patient: "Well, there is a sequel to that. Having got me to break down the woman might say 'Now I can tell you what an effort it has been to get you . . . how much I want you.' "

Analyst: "In the contest between you as the man and a woman one possible conclusion is that you break down. Could not there be another conclusion, namely, that the woman breaks down?"

Patient: "Yes, but then it has to start differently. Instead of starting by saying 'I don't need you, I am indifferent, you cannot break me down,' it would have to start by my trying to break the woman down. She would say 'I want you so terribly; if you go, it will kill me.' Then I would stick my chest out and strut about the place. That is how I wanted my mother to be, but if the woman became like that, like mother has become in my later life, it would make her taboo on that very account. Besides it is not the way a mother should be. As a child I wanted her to be like that, but I can't bear it now."

The first significant thing about these recent sessions is the fact that the patient, having for several months used the analyst in the role of the father-image and having thereby revived and analysed the essential ingredients of his emotional fixation to his father, now immediately proceeds to use the analyst as one hundred per cent. mother-image, playing out his emotional life with his mother within the analytical sessions and succeeding eventually in spite of protracted resistances in reviving the memories of these emotional contests of his infant life with mother.

The importance of this stage of his analysis in the process of analytical amelioration cannot be over-estimated, for it is his mother-fixation, or rather his fixation in this emotional pattern as played out in infancy with mother, which prevents him from developing a practicable or satisfactory emotional relationship with any woman in the present day.

The material has been given in some detail because analytical experience shows us that it is only by permitting the mind to follow the line of least resistance through Free Association of Thought which firstly results in the patient unwittingly experiencing and acting out his early emotional sequences towards the analyst, and secondly it is only by a recognition of what he is doing and an increasing insight into it that his otherwise blind ego can be brought to bear upon the matter, and to appreciate how throughout his life it has been and still is the victim of such emotional fixations that prevent an adequate adjustment to reality, including the reality of his sexual needs, and thereby effectively prevent his reaching not only his emotional goal, but also every purpose of every level of his psyche.

The importance of mother-fixation as a complete frustration to the adaptation of the mind to love interest and life, is due to its splitting of the mother need from the need of the sexual instinct, and to a consequent regression of the emotional energy back to the patterns which the child originally played out with his mother. The splitting deprives the mental transferences of the greater part of their potential dynamic energy and, worse than this, includes a sense of frustration in any and every transference relationship. Like the child, the adult is liable to give up the hopeless struggle for satisfaction in life and to resort to sulks or its equivalent, assumed indifference, not recognizing the primitive or instinct source of his failure to find anything in life satisfactory.

The few sessions here recorded since we dealt with the analysis and dissipation of this patient's father-fixations show us the beginning of the unravelling and dissipation of the patient's mother-fixation, of the emotional patterns which were formed in infancy during his relationship to his mother and which have since absorbed the greater part of his mental-emotional libido, whilst his sexual life has remained apparently dissociated from them but actually on an unconscious plane a part of them; and any sexual act whether masturbatory or otherwise had therefore no possible contact with any real world or with any real person in that world. In consequence, as reality relationships were deprived of a fundamental instinct source of energy, life was futile. No purpose was sufficiently stimulating to make it worth while.

It is an interesting reflection that without this instinct satisfaction or its psychical equivalent not only does life seem futile, but it is only a matter of time (one generation) for it to become extinct. A "cancer" of the soul has set in and the body eats or burns itself up in the course of one individual lifetime.

We have seen the beginning of the undoing of these patterns responsible for the essential disorder of this patient's mind. He has told us the only solution would be to throw all these patterns overboard and to start out again.

Will he do so?

"Can a man enter the second time into his mother's womb and be born?"

We shall see.

Chapter XXI

The Relief of Mother-Fixation

IN SEVERAL of the recorded sessions, and particularly in the last three or four chapters, we have had a demonstration of the all important transference[1] situation, and, partially at least, of its interpretation and dispersion.

For instance, early in Chapter XX the patient discovered through his indifference to the analyst (an assumed indifference due to intense emotional frustration i.e. due to the opposite of indifference) exactly why he sulked with his mother in infancy. We saw also that his assumed indifference towards contemporary women in his present-day life, an attitude and technique which robbed him of the possibility of friendly heterosexual relationships, was a repetition of the sulking tactics of childhood. Thus he had proceeded from an acting out of his previously predominant father-fixation pattern to an acting out and a revelation of his underlying mother-fixation.

The uncovering of the emotional pattern of his fixation to the mother-image proceeded apace and occupied a considerable number of his subsequent sessions. For instance, we had a succession of dream material of which the following dream is an example and an epitome of the psychological pattern uncovered, revealed and enacted during this stage of his analysis.

"*I had been to a theatre to some show or other and when it was over I was taking one of the performers, a young woman, away with me. It was rather dark and late and we were hurrying to catch a train. Then it seems it was mother I was hurrying along with to catch the train. Apparently the young woman had changed into mother.*"

[1] The transference will be explained later in this chapter (see pp, 226-7).

He had no difficulty in interpreting the essentials of this dream.

He said: "It shows that mother wins in the end. One part of me tries to take up with the other woman and the other part of me apparently wants mother; that is why it changes. The deeper or more powerful part of me gets its way. Mother must be the deeper part. I can now see that throughout my life I have lacked the potency to make the winning of a girl complete, and that is *because my potency is not on tap for anybody but mother*. On the other hand, the powerful sexual instinct, the more or less unconscious thing that rivets one to a woman and makes a marriage, has been on account of my fixation to mother getting an outlet in phantasy only—probably, as some of my dreams suggest, a necessarily unconscious phantasy of intimacy with mother. The outward and visible sign of this has been my acts of masturbation or their equivalent. But in spite of mother being a frustration on the sexual plane, the need of her has in some form or other remained— perhaps in the form of the need for a sort of companion- ship, a companionship which seems to involve a repression of all emotions and urges except in so far as she will release them. So it becomes necessary for whatever com- panion I am with to release the urge before I am conscious of any. It seems to me that more than permission is required for the release of this urge. It requires some positive encouragement on the part of the other person. Anyhow, I have found throughout my life that I am passive unless the other person does something about it. It seems to be spontaneity that is lacking. I still rely on my companion to make the suggestions. If I do go so far as to make any suggestions myself it is only if he or she had previously indicated that that is what was wanted.

"Nevertheless, if I am alone there is something missing. I need that companion, that someone to lean on. It is the equivalent of the missing mother of infancy that I need. The child tags itself on to its mother. If mother is missing there is only one incentive and that is to find mother and to tag oneself on to her. So it seems that as far as any spontaneous urge or impetus is concerned in life I am still a baby. This was my only impulse or incentive—to find the mother equivalent. So before I came to see you I was suffering from an inadequacy or absence of any spontaneous urge or drive in life with one exception and that exception was to find mother or a substitute for her. It was that spontaneous drive, the only one from within me, that led me to seek and find you. That accounts for my coming for analysis. This need of somebody is the one and only positive thing, though it too I have attempted to deny; in fact, I denied it even in action in so far as I made myself leave my mother."

Analyst: "So your *ego* broke with mother, but that was no guarantee that your *id* would leave her. You have, as you recognize, been ever since fixated to her, though admittedly the fixation has not been that overwhelmingly positive thing which causes an adult man to grow up in contentment with his mother. On the contrary, even at the deeper levels there has been considerable conflict in connection with your attachment to mother. One might say that you are still id-conflict fixated to mother. It is an ambivalent fixation. There is more frustration than gratification in it. Hence the feeling of irksomeness in her presence."

Patient: "Up to the age of twenty-one I still lived with my mother and now I appreciate that there was present a sort of emotional friction. I don't mean the irritation to which you refer and which became more marked as time went on. By friction I mean the rubbing of the emotions."

The patient here burst into laughter at his unexpressed Free Association of Thought to the terms he had used, first "friction" and then when he tried to amend it, "rubbing." He muttered under his breath "Confound it, cannot one get away from these revolting intimate terms!" And then aloud: "Well, I suppose it *was* this unconscious goings-on with mother that mattered. Anyhow, there was plenty of

activity in my life while I lived with her. I had more zest
for living than I have had since. Since then I suppose I
have suffered from a sort of bereavement and have not
rubbed with anybody, at least not with anybody that
mattered, unless it has been quite recently since I came
for analysis and started the process again, though inadequately, with you.

"At twenty-one I did not appreciate how strong the
continual emotional stimulus of my mother was, but I
somehow felt I was only maintaining a state of conflict, a
state of irritation, with something fundamentally wrong
about it. I felt I must get away. I knew I had better leave
her. My trouble is that I have found no alternative to her.
I realize now that the ego cannot help one essentially in
this matter any more than it enabled me to overcome my
conflict merely by the effort of leaving her on the reality
plane. I think it was chiefly my ego that did this parting.
As you know, my ego had taken up a great deal of the
function of ruling and ordering my life. I was conscious of
the situation of the only son and the mother, and I had
seen around me the sort of unsatisfactory results it led to.
My idiot of an ego thought I had only to leave her and I
would find a solution, not realizing that my id remained
fixed.

"Well, as you know, I have found no alternative to
mother. If only I could put this right everything would be
right. My present position is inadequate drive or incentive, libido I suppose you would call it, and I would say
also an inadequacy of emotions. At least it is an inadequacy
until someone comes along and makes me feel something.
It strikes one as a sort of emotional dependence that a
child has upon its parents, to be tagged on to something
bigger and stronger than itself. I think now of the way a
dog follows its master about and is completely lost without
him, and further how it is emotionally dependent upon
such things as a pat on its head from his hand. I think too
of the way a child follows its mother about and how it
would lose interest and incentive in life if it were deprived

of that mother. So it would seem that I came to you very much at the emotional level of an infant in arms, or rather I should say of a toddler.

"The sort of lust for living which grown-up people around me appear to have is lacking. Maybe it is that my instincts have withdrawn their power from all courses of action and perhaps it is this withdrawal that makes it seem like a veto. Should I go back to mother having recognized how dependent I am emotionally upon her? I could again share my interests and my talks with her, and I am sure I would become a much more active person through bringing mother into all my emotional life. Of course, I would have what I heard one woman refer to contemptuously as an 'itchy navel,' but no doubt mothers prefer men like this (i.e. babies) as much as the woman who made this remark prefers them to have an itch somewhere else. It is all a question of biased judgment.

"Against going back to mother is the fact that my ego recognizes that men who do this remain emotionally filial, undeveloped like I am. But that is not all, for even emotionally mother is almost impossible for me, except in phantasy, because in actual experience she is my intellectual inferior, tiresome and irritating.

"I can see the structure behind all this. There are as it were three levels at work. The upper, ego or reality level, says 'leave mother.' So that is what I did. Beneath this there is a sort of upper unconscious level which, like the ego, will not turn the potency on for mother—unless it is doing so in the acts of masturbation. But the trouble is the deepest unconscious level which still loves mother and *won't let the potency flow for anybody else.* It is still as it were wedded to mother.

"In choosing another woman I am rendered impotent by this deeper level, the source and custodian of my potency, which wants relations with mother only and does not want it with any other woman. This deep source of my energy is vague about most things, but seemingly it does know the smell of mother and nobody else will do.

"Generally speaking I can only talk from my upper or ego level and from that level I have no doubt that mother is a tiresome old woman. I have left her—apparently in all but the most fundamental sense. I see now that the irritation she causes me to feel may be due to this deep level, the source of my potency, wanting relations with her, this being of course most completely repressed by the upper unconscious levels. And so an irksome conflict is created in my unconscious. All my ego is aware of is the emerging irritation and the conclusion that I must leave her.

"As we have discovered, the effect of leaving her is emotionally something like the effect of a bereavement. I am like a much-wedded man who has just lost his wife. He has little or no incentive for living. There is no enthusiasm about anything—least of all about finding a substitute for the lost love.

"That was the trouble which brought me to consult you in the first place. Having tried to put you in her place, as I previously tried to put father in her place and finally to put you in father's place, and thereby gain a new lease of enthusiasm for living, I have now seen through it all and through the patterns which underlie it.

"It has been a hell of an experience.

"The hell has been my blind, stupid and insistent attempt to make you take the place of the missing mother, as I previously tried to make you take the place of the missing father. I have nearly broken myself trying blindly and persistently to make you not only into that essential companion and guide, to tag myself on to you like a baby to its mother, but most ridiculously of all to coerce you into stimulating and gratifying all my emotional and instinctual needs. Of course, I did not realize while I was doing it that this was my persistent endeavour, and that my sulks, pretended indifference and other defences, and particularly my hatred and temper were because you would not play. The hell has been the experience of my utter frustration in these blind, instinctive endeavours to

P

relieve myself, to cure myself, by such a ridiculous and
impossible adjustment. The hell has been having to
abandon these futile attempts—to abandon them for life.
With my insight into them and my abandonment of
them, or rather I should say with my release from their
blind compulsive force, I am a sadder but a wiser man.
Indeed, I am a man, or almost a man, instead of that
persistent baby for ever needing a daddy or a mummy to
tag itself on to and suffering emotional storms because it
was so difficult to get anyone to play the desired role."

Thus we see that it was through experiencing the
transference situation in analysis that this patient finally
obtained insight into his emotional patterns, into their
source, their origin and their impracticability. He saw, as
he could have seen by no other means, that a persistence
in these patterns was for ever doomed to utter failure.
But maybe it was the experience as much as the insight
that released him from their compulsive domination over
him.

The transference, it should be explained, is that stage of
analysis when emotional attitudes (largely a mixture of
love and hate) on the part of the patient towards his
analyst dominate the picture and seem to exclude all
other material. These current experiences are shown by
interpretation and direct association to be nothing more
or less than identical emotional experiences, since repressed and forgotten, which the patient originally felt
towards his parents in infancy, and which laid the foundation of his emotional pattern and character. He has
been blindly and compulsively re-enacting them ever
since, hitherto without insight. Through the insight now
gained actually while he is re-experiencing them, and
through the nascent intensity of the emotional experience,
a vivid memory of his since forgotten childhood is revived
and the force of the compulsion to behave in this manner
is relieved. In short, the hitherto unalterable emotional
pattern is undone and the threads of it are available to
form a new pattern more in keeping with his internal

needs and external realities. The essence of cure is this heating up of the old castings and the welding of them into new shapes.

From this description it may be appreciated by the reader that no mere description of analysis is adequate to convey to an unanalysed person the mechanism of cure. This is because cure lies essentially in emotional *experiences*, together with the establishment of bridges between the current emotions and the memories of their original creation in infancy, thus leading to the most complete insight into oneself.

In Chapter XVIII, "The Climax," the patient discovered whilst vividly experiencing the emotions that his, at first sight rational, hatred of his analyst was nothing more or less than his infantile and adolescent hatred of a father-image that would not play his emotional games and gratify his instinct needs. The revelation of this uncovered the even more completely forgotten emotional relationship to the mother-image and, behold, he found it was the identical emotional pattern! It had originally been called into being through his instinctual appetites for his mother, and subsequently, through frustration and failure, transferred more hopefully on to his father. The last transference of these patterns, namely, the one on to his analyst, gave us the opportunity of exploding all his vain hopes by making them conscious and relating them to their origins.

Thus his early emotional life which had come forward into the present day, had entered into his relationship to his analyst and been re-experienced within his analytical sessions. It was gradually traced back, first to uncover forgotten memories of his attachment to his father, and soon after to uncover this relationship to his original love-object, the mother of his infancy, and to expose the fact that deep down in his unconscious his emotional potency was still fixated to this original object-choice (mother) except in so far as a modicum of it had obtained an outlet in feelings towards father, father-figures and analyst.

Analysis reversed the process which life had carried forward. The past was made so vividly conscious that the energies fixated in it were liberated for more adequate use in present emotional relationships.

Instead of loving mother exclusively in unconscious phantasy, he became capable not only of some affection for his real, living mother, but also of loving real persons, even persons in the image of mother (women) in conscious present-day life.

The sequel to this process will be revealed in the next chapter.

Chapter XXII

The Final Stage

FROM THE MINOR CLUES of this patient's present-day attitudes towards his analyst we have uncovered not only the great intensity of feeling once experienced towards his father, but also the infinitely more important original form of these emotional patterns in their nascent state as they were first called into being in his relationship to his original love-object, the mother of his babyhood. The important matter is that in this form their greatest potential intensity had remained tied up and repressed, and thus ever since inaccessible for transference to potential love-objects in his present-day life.

These persistent infantile patterns, now clearly recognized as mother-fixations rather than father-fixations, were again and again experienced during analysis towards his analyst until the working through of them eventually began to produce modifications. That they were the same patterns, albeit with a different object-choice, was made abandantly clear by the fact that he often used the very same words to describe the feelings of his mother-fixation as he had previously used to describe his desperate struggle to gain more hopeful responses from his father-image.

The emergence of his repressed and unconsciously incestuous mother-love was introduced, as is so often the case, by an interminable amount of dream material. For instance, he dreamt that he was with a very attractive woman dressed only in a little negligee.

He said: "I was excited about her. I kept wanting to do things with her. We went down to bathe and sat on a bank at the edge of a lake and I nearly fell in; but not so nearly as I did off that pier or off that theatre balcony in the other dreams. I recovered my balance all right. Later in the dream I seemed to remember her legs clasped round one of mine and it was going to be even nicer; but somehow I woke up."

An important augury of the future is that he associated his feelings in the dream to his feelings for a widow of his recent acquaintance, but of the attractive woman in the dream he says "She was not this young widow at all. I don't know who she was. All I know is that I had a feeling of wanting and longing"—he hastens to add "Not sexual —like I felt for my mother when I was with her last week."

Those who are unacquainted with analysis can hardly be expected to appreciate the importance of the association of the unknown woman to his mother on the one hand, and through his feelings for her towards a recent female acquaintance.

The fact that his association of this unknown woman to mother was through the feeling tone of the dream, and also the fact that it came unwittingly, both testify to its veracity. Further his denial that it was sexual is interesting especially in the face of the dream evidence of its intense sexuality admixed with a diminishing castration anxiety.

Reflecting on the dream he says with a significance that reveals that the memories of his first love (mother) are not going to be recalled without a struggle against resistances:

"I suppose what will have to happen is that I shall have to bring up this passionate love for my mother here—just as I felt it in my early life. Like when I cried about my father here.

"I don't know if I want to go into this emotional world at all.

"I might as well confess how glad I was to see my mother last week, and how much I liked her. I had more feelings about her than I can remember having had since I was a youngster. I am now thinking that she was saying to me: 'you are only a little baby, you poor poop . . . I don't like you at all . . . you are just a punchinello."

He broke off here a little bewildered: "I really was not

distinguishing whether I was talking about my mother or that young widow friend of mine."

Later he dreamt of an arid desert going through which he came across a place like Ascot with a party of gay ladies. He said of this:

"When I crossed the desert I left mother behind." And then, reflectingly: "Desert and desert ever since! This cultural cloak of gaiety does not touch me because my emotions are still fixated, so they are not displaceable.

"If we could bring up this feeling then all my problems would be solved. The question is how to bring it up."

Analyst: "You are doing everything in your power to suppress it."

Patient: "It would be so dangerous. It would be like exposing the bare nerve. It would be so vulnerable . . .''

To indicate the relationship of this emotional pattern to his analytical transference, and the relationship of the transference to repression of the early form of the pattern I will refer to a dream of which he said:

"I came to analysis and I think it was a woman analyst here. I said 'No, I don't want you, I want Dr. Berg.' So I climbed out of the window and jumped into the area. I was trying to find you, but I found myself knocking at the young widow's door. She said I could come in. She kissed me, and said she was terribly glad to see me."

In association to this dream he said:

"The more my affection for mother becomes uncovered the more fond I find myself becoming of other women. For the first time in my life I rang up a woman friend on my own initiative today.

"The core of my personal problem is that my sexual emotion is buried with mother and that is because it is too closely identified with mother. I felt that when I met her recently. I felt that I liked her, that she was a grand woman, very nice indeed and that seemed to free me to do other things."

Regarding the modification of his mother-fixation, I can

save space by emphasizing that it and all other impractical emotional attitudes followed in their pattern of resolution exactly the same lines as did the resolution of his father attachment. The climax of this process has been detailed in Chapter XVIII. It included the working up to actual emotional experience of these feelings towards his analyst during the sessions, with subsequent insight into them and vivid memories of their inception and origin, together with a recognition of their impracticability in their original form. In the same way as he felt exasperation and hatred for his analyst as a non-responsive father-image, he again felt it when he had placed him in the role of an unresponsive mother-image. Again it had to be accurately interpreted, successfully enough for the patient automatically to remember as a vivid experience phases of infancy when he had reacted thus towards a frustrating mother, sufficiently accurately for the patient to realize that he was still acting thus towards all emotional attachments in his current life.

These were the basic or most strongly charged emotional patterns hitherto unaltered since infancy. There were, of course, other patterns of a minor or accessory nature which by the same process underwent concurrent modification. In general, it may be said that the divergence between his unconscious emotional patterns on the one side and his relatively well developed ego and reason on the other became no longer a divergence. The former were fully recognized and in their modified form infinitely more acceptable to his conscious or ego levels. In other words he was no longer constantly at cross purposes with himself.

It cannot be too strongly emphasized that all these changes were rendered possible only through the real experience of his fundamental emotions and passions within the transference situation. The assumption of many unanalysed persons that deep-seated emotional changes can be brought about simply by an intellectual analysis of them, an assumption which many patients cherish during the early stages of analysis, must be exploded. The analyst has to endure many sessions from all patients in which the intellectual pretences of the ego hold the field while the emotional needs of the id are treated as though they do not exist.

The difference between an intellectualized "analysis" and a real analysis is the difference between cant and life, ego and id, man and God—the difference between pretence and cure. The ego is for ever pretending and dissembling; so we have to wait until the gloves are off and the emotional fight is on.

However hysterical this emotional fight may be, hysteria is analytically remediable, whereas on the other hand the state of intellectual armour or cant, or pretence, or denial of the existence of the emotional undercurrent is a state of mind which is not curable until it is exploded. This is why the analyst rejoiced in Chapter XVIII when he discovered that this patient was at last bringing his emotional life into the analysis, for he knew that now big emotional changes were on the way.

In due course modification set in. With a recognition in full consciousness of his previously repressed desires for his mother, and the cause of his irritability towards her in their necessary frustration in that direction, the libidinal energy of these desires was at last released from repression, and his feelings towards persons in the image of his mother had gradually added to them the energy previously locked up in the intolerable frustrations of mother-fixation.

Thus his heterosexual libido, never entirely absent, became enormously energized, and he found himself with an increasing drive, impulse, or incentive towards female acquaintances who had previously meant very little to him from an emotional point of view.

The difficulty in making the reader appreciate the mechanism of this will be better realized when I say that the patient himself, despite his insight, was frequently at a loss to understand it. On occasions he was bewildered, if not amazed.

He said to me: "I spent an evening with Phyllis the other day, and do you know I felt quite different about her. Indeed, I did not invite her to my rooms as I have done in the past, although she expected it, because I felt that the emotional experience of having her there alone with me would be more than I could bear. Far from asking her whether we should have intimacy before supper or after it as I had done in the past and wondering how to go about it, I felt now that I could not gauge what on earth would happen if I had her alone. I felt it might be cataclysmic, if not catastrophic—beyond my power of control. I dared not risk it."

It may be easy to appreciate that with his newly-released libido, released as I have said from mother-fixation, it was not long before he found the woman whom he could not resist.

When I said earlier that it was the experience (within analysis) as much as the insight that *released* him from the compulsive domination of his earlier emotional patterns, I may have overstated the truth. These patterns were, of course, only *modified*. Just a slight modification (though heaven knows difficult enough to achieve) is necessary to transfer the pattern, with slight alterations, from the original object choice (mother) to another individual in the same form (woman) and presumably with the same "smell." The apparently astounding difference is due to the enormous release of libido previously repressed through the original frustration. With this change of object, frustration is no more. The intense longing accumulating with compound interest since infancy now sees the possibility of a much overdue gratification.

He has left his old compulsion of repeating the mother-fixation deadlock, but the libido of this compulsion has been released and he now rushes into the new compulsion of his biological purpose. Not only have the super-ego and ego (the reality principle) given their consent, but the energy necessary for the incentive and for attaining this end in the reality world has escaped repression and is moving along the fundamental channels laid down by generations of ingrained and inherited instincts, like the sap moving irresistibly through the trunk and branches of a tree to produce its flower and fruit.

All this happened many, many years ago, though I have transcribed some of it into current form to maintain a topical interest.

Even his parting with his analyst was not that great wrench which he had previously anticipated. He said to me:

"The emotional life which I have been leading lately makes these visits to you ridiculously tame and truly unnecessary. Even while here, and although I do not come very often, I am thinking of the time when I can get away and be with the most charming girl I have ever known in my life."

He had met many charming girls previously in his life, but had not been charmed. He had been relatively insusceptible. It may be observed here that though the libido had been released from mother-fixation, the original pattern or that fundamental form of it which throughout the generations requires another human being, much as an infant requires its mother, is, like an instinct itself, too deeply ingrained to be subject to analytical change. He still required somebody on whom to tag his libido. The only difference was that this somebody was no longer a sexually prohibited mother-image or father-image. He had reverted to a more primitive, or normal type. Like every normal person he found that the need for a companion in life, a twin soul if you like, is as necessary to the adult as mother is to the infant. Perhaps the most important change was that he ceased to resist this need.

He left his analyst with only a tinge of regret and only a tinge of hostility. The transference had been almost completely analysed away. As I have said, this was many years ago and he has since married the girl who became charming, charming enough to become his wife and the mother of his child. So from tagging on to mother, from his mother love, he has performed the normal transfer of tagging himself on to the love of somebody in the image of mother. The interesting psychological change, as distinct from the biological, is that he is at the same time acquiring an adequate incentive in life possibly as a result of the parental wife-image support and direction.

Subsidiary patterns in his main emotional trend have not completely disappeared. They have, as one would expect, undergone sublimation into social, professional and business activities. He still has a healthy appreciation of men friends, with the old characteristic of a leaning towards older men. But the interest in this and other directions is very much decreased or rather it is now secondary to and indeed dependent upon the main direction of his libidinal life, namely, being supported and gratified in his marital situation. In short, one might say that it is *because* the mother-wife or wife-mother is at home that all is well with the world and that other interests are appetizing, stimulating and worth pursuing.

I have endeavoured to explain to some extent the theory of how the ground was prepared for these changes, of what it was that set the ball rolling and began the change within him of which these external events finally became the outward and visible sign. It should, however, be remembered that the *theory* of cure is one thing, and the fact of cure is another. In some of our apparently most successful cases analyst as well as patient are both befogged as to the mechanism which produced results which were beyond their dreams. On the other hand, one meets with cases where every inch of ground appears to have been covered and uncovered and perfectly understood by both parties alike, without achieving appreciable therapeutic results. Insight alone is rarely sufficient to bring about more than very slight amelioration, and sometimes with the fullest insight amelioration of symptoms is the slightest.

In this particular case it may be said that analysis did not cure the patient. It merely released some imprisoned libido which in accordance with the laws of nature and the inherited instinct patterns immediately sought a "cure" for its new-found appetite in the appropriate biological manner and with due regard for the reality world of our environmental pattern of civilization.

In other words, he cured himself by seeking and finding an object for his newly-released and nascent libidinal or psycho-sexual need. In the last instance it is life that cures, not analysis.

Notwithstanding all the care and compendiousness of our transcription of this analysis, as we have not ourselves been able to experience emotionally what the patient under analysis experienced, we remain infinitely short of a true revelation of the daily, hourly, minutely details in all their voluminousness—details which the subject of analysis alone can emotionally experience, and in which alone can lie the appreciation of something as indescribable as life itself. Can life—the experience of living—be described to anyone or to anything that has not itself lived? Life has to be lived to be known, and analytical amelioration has to be experienced to be appreciated.

In the meantime our former patient had become too busy appreciating life to reflect upon the trials and tribulations of his analysis. Even his previous interests in masses of more or less occult literature no longer preoccupied him. He was concerned in living as living itself was the only sufficient gratification for his new-found hunger for it.

In short, he had inherited life, and life was already in process of inheriting him.

Chapter XXIII

Theoretical Review

It HAS been seen how much of a theoretical nature can be gleaned from the analytical study of a single patient, but it is difficult for an analyst to confine his conclusions to the evidences produced by one solitary case study. Different cases will emphasize different kinds of mental mechanism, each throwing its own particular light on some specific aspect of psychic structure. In due course certain common principles of the functioning of the deeper levels of the mind emerge which seem to have universal application.

In the case we have been studying the cardinal presenting symptom, namely inadequacy of an integrated or ego-syntonic heterosexual drive or potency, at first suggested to me that his Oedipus complex was deficient in energy, that quantities of libido had failed to reach genital organization, and that in consequence he would not arrive at a transference stage adequate to result in much amelioration or even adequate to maintain a continuance of treatment.

At times it seemed that these early conclusions would prove correct and the patient would break off treatment at various stages of prematurity owing to his lack of transference attachment to the analyst. Perhaps one of the most surprising results was that, far from the transference proving inadequate, a large proportion of the analytical time was devoted to transference phenomena. However deficient the Oedipus organization had been, it certainly proved to be the nucleus of our difficulties as it was of the patient's extra-analytical difficulties. In consequence, although his case material provides much evidence of the nature and structure of the Oedipus complex, it is insufficient to provide a full therotetical construction of the pre-Oedipus levels of mental organization.

Nevertheless, it is necessary in a theoretical review to introduce a reference to these earlier levels though admittedly the justification for this lies mostly in material other than that presented by this particular case.

ORGANIZATION AND VICISSITUDES OF THE LIBIDO

ORAL LEVEL:

Whatever life urges or possible libidinal urges are responsible for cell-division and for the behaviour of the oösperm resulting in the intra-uterine growth of the foetus, when finally after the period of gestation this foetus is born at term, it soon exhibits a very definite drive or lust at an oral level. Its pleasure urges appear to be predominantly oral and its essential interest and activity that of getting the nipple into its mouth and sucking. From this alone there may be some justification for the psycho-analytical theory that the first specialized erotogenic zone is oral and the primary exhibition of the libidinal urge is in the activities of sucking.

But psycho-analytical conclusions are based upon clinical material alone and this theory came about through the discovery of its importance from the study of many cases under analysis. In our particular case one of the few references to the influence of the oral activities and frustrations in forming the patient's love and hate patterns and in contributing to his character formation is given in Chapter XIX where he says: "You would not feed me—just as my mother suddenly refused to continue her feeding of me. Apparently I have wanted you to respond in the same way as for a long time I wanted my mother to respond, by putting me to the breast again. If she had done, by Jove, wouldn't I have bitten her! It occurs to me now that I did bite her once or twice for keeping me waiting, for frustrating me, and that was the origin of my hate. When she would not put me to the breast again my hate grew. I suffered, became miserable, as I have done here." This is elaborated in the footnote on the same page: "We thus see the origin of hate from oral frustration, e.g. through an inadequate supply of milk. No doubt it is later reinforced by anal and genital frustrations."

Another, though this time indirect, reference to the oral level is made in his dream of the crocodile (Chapter IX). As is mentioned later in that chapter, this is a *projection*, in form of the image of the crocodile with its sharp teeth, of his oral, sadistic, biting stage of libidinal development.

Psycho-analysts believe that to the infant at the oral-sadistic (biting) stage the world consists (in its phantasy) of "breasts and bellies"; meaning that its libidinal interest is to devour the objects it loves (e.g. breasts) and even to overpower by incorporating those it hates, including the parents (cannibalistic phantasies) and at the same time through a projection of these phantasies on to the objects of its desire (bellies) to fear being devoured by them. Hence the creation of such dream bogies as biting crocodiles. These matters will be referred to again under "The Development of Super-ego and Ego."

ANAL LEVEL:

From this pre-eminence of the oral erotogenic zone as the primary causative agent in character formation, we pass on to the effects of anal feelings, experiences and activities in contributing to emotional patterns, tendencies and character. Clinical material bearing upon this has been given at some length in Chapters XIV and XV. The importance to our patient of retaining his fortune intact as though it were an essential integral part of himself suggests an infantile phase of reluctance to part with his faecal accumulations, a phase which has left its mark not only in his attitude to his money but also (as seen in Chapter XV) when evacuating his bowels in his tendency to exercise sufficient retentivity to get the maximum amount of feeling and pleasure from the process.

In Chapter XV it was suggested that without intellectualized or cultural outlets for libido, the infant was nevertheless living in a world of anal experiences as rich in its excitements and alarms as, and identical in the details of its emotional pattern with, those which subsequently give rise to and show themselves in our conscious thought and cultural dramatizations—as exciting and as dangerous as any which we can purchase between the covers of a 7s. 6d. novel. It makes no essential difference that at that early level it is all being lived within the isolation of its own skin, or more precisely at the orifices between this skin and the outside world, the points at which contact between the interior world and the exterior world is in actual operation, preparatory to a so-called reality, or more correctly a less material and more mental, contact with the exterior world.

The point is that an anal level of libidinal development like its oral precursor, *upon whose pattern its patterns are largely formed*, is essentially auto-erotic and has little dependence upon or reference to persons outside itself. The persons as such are called in psycho-analysis whole-objects. These early auto-erotic levels of libido have reference to part-objects such as the nipple, the thumb or similar things as aids to auto-erotic gratification, but they are not concerned with whole-objects or persons as such. Even the more advanced stage of phallic development is not necessarily related to whole-objects and the gratifications derived from it are auto-erotic and independent of love or hate, or ambivalent including both love and hate.

Urethral eroticism being, like its anal homologue dependent upon and repetitively stimulated by excretory function inevitably follows the pattern of the anal. It should be remembered that it is of special importance in forming a bridge as it were between the eroticism of excretory activities and that of the phallic and in due course genital stages of development.

THE GENITAL LEVEL:

It is only when the libido reaches the relatively high genital level of organization that the infant's psyche becomes fully aware of outside persons such as its parents, and of their loves and hates, as being of crucial importance in its pleasure life, and consequently projects its own developing love and hate to them as persons or whole-objects. Its pre-genital relationships to persons around it though embodying many manifestations of love and hate have a different mental quality, apparently one which does not take full cognizance of them as specific individuals and at the same time essential to him as potential objects of gratification. Previously its loves and hates were relatively blind and without consideration of their effect upon the persons concerned. In short, it seems that prior to the genital stage these persons are regarded more as what might be called part-objects.

It is at the genital stage of libidinal organization that there develops the all-important Oedipus complex, the nuclear basis of all subsequent whole-object relationships, the foundations of social and love life and of the dissatisfactions and neuroses connected therewith. It is this genital libidinal organization and this Oedipus complex which will determine the type and intensity of the patient's transference phenomena in the course of his analysis. His relationship to the analyst and its variations are an epitomized revelation of the pattern of his Oedipus development and of the vicissitudes through which it has passed.

The importance of this pattern for his health and happiness and the importance of its revelation, interpretation and dissolution have been amply demonstrated throughout the greater part of the case history here recorded.

Although a certain amount of his libido remained fixated to oral, anal and phallic auto-erotic levels, the nuclear psychopathology which was responsible for his lack of satisfaction, happiness and incentive in life was the Oedipus fixation of his libido to the original parent-figures and the impossibility of satisfactory relationships to other persons while this unconscious fixation remained undisturbed.

Although there is every justification for the presumption that genital organization with its resulting Oedipus complex will follow the emotional patterns previously laid down for it at the oral and anal stages, from the point of view of a person's relationship to other persons or whole-objects, a relationship which is so essential to the future adequate relief of his psycho-sexual tension, the Oedipus complex can still be regarded as the nuclear complex in the production and maintenance of the psychoneuroses.

There is, of course, no clear line of demarcation between emotional relationships developed at pre-genital levels of libidinal organization and those developed at this level. Neither is there a hard and fast line between relationships to part-objects and the evolution of this to include whole-objects or persons. There is, on the contrary, every degree of progress by graduated stages from the simplest to the most complex. Clear-cut distinctions become even more difficult to lay down when we see throughout analysis such processes as a regressive reference of patterns elaborated at later stages of organization back to the operation of more primitive component-instinct levels.

For instance, the patient's recently quoted remark about breast feeding by his mother might well include emotional patterns towards her developed at an Oedipus level and subsequently referred back, carried back as it were to the oral level of breast feeding. Similarly, the hate which he supposes originated at this level by her withholding of the breast, might be only in part true and might well derive its chief force from genital frustation at the later genital level. On a conscious plane he would naturally not talk of his hatred of mother for having frustrated his genital sexual desires, but would refer such hate back to a feeding level more acceptable on a conscious ego plane.

Thus we see that even the particular clarity of special instances in the tracing of the development of emotional patterns may be more apparent than true. Mental-

emotional growth, like physical development, although it
follows a strict sequence of cause and effect is not a one-
dimensional process; and although we are largely right in
stating that the nucleus of every neurosis, character trait,
or other emotional pattern lies within the Oedipus complex, this does not exclude its simultaneous relationship to
all the levels of pre-genital organization which are at the
same time still alive and active and which have in their
turn largely determined the particular nature of the
genital organization itself. What the infant did with his
mouth, and the oral-cannibalistic phantasies connected
with it, and what he did with his bowel function and the
innumerable omnipotent and sadistic phantasies connected with it, he will continue to do in phantasies at
every libidinal level with the whole-objects which subsequently engage his emotional attention at the Oedipus
level of libidinal development.

What will concern us, and particularly what will concern the patient, is the operation of the structure formed
within his psyche in its current relationship to the persons
and things now occupying his attention during his present-
day adult life.

DEVELOPMENT OF SUPER-EGO AND EGO

Super-Ego:

Concurrently with the organization of his libido
throughout its pre-genital and genital levels, there will
manifest itself in rapidly increasing strength a totally
different psychic force, which, however much it may
borrow its dynamic drive from libidinal sources, operates
principally in an exactly contrary manner to his primary
libidinal seekings. This new mental component is called
the super-ego. It may be regarded as absent at birth—
the libidinal urges being at that stage the only guide for
living; but there is much evidence that it comes into
being much earlier than psycho-analysis originally supposed. There is evidence that even at an oral level, life is

not so simple as it would seem. It may be that it is impossible to satisfy even the oral lusts without at the same time, or at least very soon, experiencing oral fears or anxieties. I have said that for the infant at the breast the world consists not only of breasts but also of bellies. From the first the concern of all life was not only to eat, but, in relation to the eating urges and the phantasies connected therewith, to have a lively and terrifying conception of being itself eaten. Even at this stage we have evidence that anxiety exists, or is very soon called into existence, as an inhibiting factor in the process of oral gratification. In short, wherever there is a lust or appetite to be gratified, the mind has a tendency, possibly based upon racial experience, to project some of the phantasies connected with the gratification of this lust on to the more or less frustrating environment and in consequence to regard this environment as having similar tendencies directed against itself. Thus cannibalistic phantasies cause the psyche to conceive of the world as peopled by cannibals, and similarly in the course of maturation super-ego construction progresses *pari passu* with libidinal development, and phantasies of talion punishment exert their controlling, inhibiting or castrating effects upon every stage and level of pleasure seeking.

This process reaches a climax at the stage when the infant's libido, having developed to a genital sexual level, naturally phantasies gratification with the parent of the opposite sex—naturally, since every pre-genital desire has hitherto been more or less gratified by this same parent. It is at this point that the first real and unequivocal frustration by the parent is encountered.

This total frustration reinforces a super-ego which may hitherto have had little external confirmation and encouragement of its inhibiting or castrating phantasies. Therefore it is at this point that the super-ego, having gained a new-found supremacy, sets about achieving a total "castration," destruction or repression of the recently formed Oedipus desires. This leads eventually to the disintegration of the Oedipus phantasy, and, incidentally, gives rise not only to incest taboo, but to the extreme horror connected with incest and to the "unthinkable" nature of such wishes. In all cases a varying proportion of the Oedipus phantasies are not so much disintegrated as repressed in their original form, resulting in a corresponding degree of unconscious fixation to the particular parent to whom they were principally directed.

Nothing of the nature of these psychic constellations in our particular patient's case could have been predicted with confidence prior to analytical investigation. But in the light of this investigation we can now see that Oedipus phantasies, connected with positive gratification with the mother and corresponding destruction of the father, primarily underwent such powerful repression that their pattern was no longer available to the patient for utilization by substitution of object. That is why he was incapable of any conscious phantasy of a love situation with any person in the form of mother.

Under the auspices of the super-ego, which had become supreme at this stage, he had succeeded in this repression by virtue of transferring that portion of libidinal desire which could not otherwise be dealt with on to that parent (the father) whom his super-ego forbad him to destroy. By this manœuvre he was able to satisfy to some extent both his libidinal desires and his super-ego demands, at the same time countering or reversing his libidinal aggressive hate. This was the mechanism of inversion which resulted in his forgetting, or rather being totally unconscious of, his original love for mother, and enabled him to remember only the experiences of this emotional pattern in the form of a relationship to his father.

In due course this relationship, particularly as, aided by the death of his father, it had reached a stage of unconscious sexual consummation, encountered reality and ego incompatibility and was therefore, if not totally repressed, completely inhibited. In consequence, he found himself prior to analysis quite unable to achieve any relationship with another person of either sex which could include his libidinal drive and utilize the physiological mechanisms for the regulation of psycho-sexual tension. The most he could do was to form aim-inhibited and apparently non-sexual friendships with older men in the image of father (friendships the libidinal urge of which was impoverished by sexual repression) at the same time leaving his sexual needs dissociated from his psyche and practically at the level of auto-erotic unconscious phantasy life, or at most at the level of infantile genital organization with its unconscious incestuous phantasies.

Only through the process of analysis, particularly through transference experience and its analysis, were the repressed complexes unrepressed—brought back into consciousness—and their enormous fund of energy made available for use in his reality relationship in the form in which they had originally existed, with only the usual normal change of object: from mother to wife.

EGO:

To return to the stage of development when he was in the throes of the Oedipus complex: super-ego inhibition, apparently reinforced by the friendliness of his father, had resulted in so powerful a conflict that his psyche had had no other course but to exercise repression of the whole constellation—a repression more complete and successful than is usually the case. His super-ego was satisfied, but only at the expense of an unduly complete repression and dissociation of this genital stage of libidinal organization with its relationship to a whole-object of the same sex as his mother. At the same time sexual relationship to those of his own sex was not tolerated by his ego. His psychic problem was in a sense solved, but only at the expense of a repudiation of all emotional patterns, particularly those which involved a relationship to other persons.

What was left to make life worth living? Only those aim-inhibited Oedipus levels of libidinal organization which had not undergone repression and were in consequence remembered, the component instincts, and more especially substitute gratifications on an ego plane. It was as though he had repudiated an ordinary emotional life, and built up in its place an artificial structure of ego values since these had the advantage of avoiding disturbance of the intolerable conflict, now successfully repressed. Thus he entered into what is in analysis called the latency period of life.

LATENCY PERIOD:

With the dissolution or partial dissolution of the Oedipus complex the sexual life, including its previously predominant auto-erotic components, appears to be in large part abandoned. The libido of the developing infant had progressed through the various auto-erotic stages with their emphasis on a succession of erotogenic zones until it had reached its infantile maturity in the genital stage with its whole-object relationships to the parents—an exact equivalent to mature psycho-sexual love. It is as though an increasing hope of complete libidinal satisfaction was at this point—the point of the Oedipus complex—wrecked upon the rocks of parental non-co-operation and frustration. The impression is that the whole process of increasing hope and longing were by dint of the pain of this experience more or less completely abandoned. Immediately the psycho-sexual substitute satisfactions, games and sublimations, the conscious symbolic substitutes never totally absent, are thereupon enormously reinforced. They are, as it were, the straws at which the drowning libido clutches.

The infant with external encouragement instead of frustration in this field learns to get its sexuality-equivalent substitutive thrills from these interests and activities which it finds can be openly and consciously indulged. Whether it be swinging, romping, games of hide-and-seek and all the rest, it is experiencing thrills and internal excitements which at this stage of development act as more or less effective substitutes for the now repressed erotic phantasies, and act as precursors and nuclei for the future excitements and libidinal satisfactions both of a cultural and of a sexual nature. It is this part of its emotional life which is socially accepted and which need not be repressed. Therefore, it is this part of life which occupies the field of consciousness and embodies within itself the emotional patterns of the now repressed and unconscious allo-erotic and auto-erotic phantasies.

The evidence for this point of view is the evidence of clinical psycho-analytical experience, contrasted with the ordinary overt manifestations of life's activities and the pre-occupations of the conscious level of mental functioning. Whereas surface observation reveals that the human mind is consciously concerned with the gadgets of civilized life and custom, *this apparent and conscious world is shown both biologically and analytically to be merely the cypher in which the libido, still fundamentally primitive in its aims, writes or describes its patterns and its strivings (together with their repressing influences) essentially unaltered since its earliest days of auto-erotic and allo-erotic tensions, reliefs and frustrations.*

Moreover, it is shown analytically that since our earliest years of infancy our minds have as it were entered into a socially dictated conspiracy of silence, blindness and even repudiation regarding the sensuous world which was previously our main preoccupation. It is as though convention had insisted that we remove ourselves so thoroughly from our past "sinful" tendencies that we must as it were acquire and maintain a blind spot regarding them and even regarding their observation and recognition, especially, and this also has its significance, in the infants around us. Our insight is limited to that which is socially and conventionally acceptable. This process of repression, cumulative since the dissolution or repression of the Oedipus complex, can usually only be undone by a personal experience of analysis. This is the explanation revealed by psycho-analysis of why this primitive world remains to most people unseen and incredible.

In the case of our patient, infancy and its compulsions

and fears were put aside to an unusually successful degree whilst he took flight into the symbols of culturally constructed values. He lived largely on an ego plane. He was the bright boy at school. Personal relationships became relatively meaningless, and the symbols of culture and scholastic attainment were, so far as he was able, put in their place.

This compensatory mechanism was moderately successful until he outgrew the years of scholastic achievement, until he parted from the only contact he had maintained, namely that with his mother; in short, until he grew up, or was expected both by others and himself to have grown up.

It was principally then that he discovered that something was missing. He knew not what it was, but, armed with an excellent ego, he presented himself for analysis. Gradually he found out. He found out in a sense which only analysis could help him to find out; that is to say not merely in the sense of ego discovery—which would have been the equivalent of telling him what was the matter without the slightest indication that anything could be done about it—he found out in the sense that he became conscious of forces of which he had since infancy been totally unaware.

These forces became not only conscious, but also gratifiable in a way which enabled him to adjust them to the realities around him, real persons in a real world, and utilize them for his much-needed and overdue libidinal, super-ego and psycho-sexual satisfactions. It is only by this utilization that he could achieve that regulation of psychic and libidinal tensions which is essential for the maintenance of nervous health and of mental-emotional well-being.

Thus the infant's incestuous dream of consummating all the previously enjoyed pre-genital libidinal desires at their reinforced Oedipus stage of development had no longer to be repudiated *in toto* with the resulting feeling not only of their castration, but of the repudiation of all that made life livable. He could now escape the ever-increasing depression which is the inevitable sequel of this process. This unconscious dream, the longing for mother, had now become realizable for him by the normal and very simple process of the *change of object*, its least essential element. By this means he was able to enter into the happiness of marital union not merely as a form, but as a complete psycho-sexual experience, and with it to find life itself.

His analysis had demonstrated that an individual cannot repress and deny the psycho-sexual libidinal force which created him without at the same time denying that which maintains his present health and happiness. For they are one and the same force. There is no such thing as "successful repression." He had learnt that obedience to nature's compulsion is a necessary condition of life—both racial and individual. He had learnt to unrepress and utilize the hitherto dammed-up libidinal drive of this compulsion.

Instead of being dead wood on a parent tree he could now become part of the living structure conducting the sap and bearing the fruit.

The psychological emancipation of this ex-patient may be further gauged by the fact that, in spite of his attainment of a position of national eminence, he has consented to the publication of this much of the past and now obsolete record of his metamorphosis.

GLOSSARY

AETIOLOGY: The science of causation.

AFFECT: The energy of an emotion. It may be aroused by a variety of stimuli and is capable of displacement on to concepts with which it was not originally associated.

AIM-INHIBITED: The aim of an instinct is relief of tension; for instance in the sexual instinct it is orgasm. The aim is said to be inhibited where the psyche is influenced by the instinct without expectation or cognizance of its aim, for instance in apparently non-sexual (e.g. child-parent) love and in the pleasure of sociability, particularly with one's own sex.

ALLO-EROTIC: The adjective of allo-erotism: erotism directed to another person. (Cf. auto-erotism.)

AMBIVALENCE: The simultaneous existence of opposing affects, usually love and hate, directed towards the same person or object. One or both of the affects may be unconscious.

AMNESIA: A memory blank.

ANAL EROTIC: The adjective of anal erotism: pleasurable sensations experienced through the act of defecation, or other stimulation of the anus, especially enjoyed in childhood and repressed later.

ANAL SPHINCTER: The circular muscle which surrounds the anal opening.

ANALYSAND: One who is being treated by analysis.

AUTO-EROTIC: The adjective of auto-erotism: Self-generated erotic stimulation without resort to another person. (Cf. Allo-erotism: erotism directed to another.)

CANNIBALISTIC: Pertaining to cannibalism or the eating of one's kind. There is psycho-analytical evidence that ontogenetically as well as phylogenetically the individual passes through a stage, associated with the development of teeth, at which he "deals with" persons and the affects they arouse in him by the phantasy of devouring them.

CASTRATION: Removal of the organs of generation.

CASTRATION COMPLEX: An unconscious fear of castration, or of any injury to the sex organs, to the person or his possessions or separation from any desired person, object or gratification.

CATHEXIS: A charge of emotional energy investing an idea or object.

CENTRIFUGAL: In a direction away from the centre.

CENTRIPETAL: In the direction toward the centre.

CLINICAL: Originally, of or pertaining to the sick bed, and hence to do with observation of the actual patient, as distinct from theoretical constructions.

COMPLEX: A group of affectively charged ideas which, through conflict, have become repressed into the unconscious.

COMPONENT-INSTINCTS: The primitive components and fore-runners of the organized genital-sexual instinct. They include pleasure-seeking impulses at every extra-genital erotogenic zone, particularly mouth, anus, urethra, and even the genital organ in so far as it is satisfied with part-objects.

CONFLICT: "War" between opposing elements in the mind.

CONSTELLATION: Any group or pattern of associated ideas with their accompanying affective investments, not necessarily repressed. (Cf. Complex.)

CYCLOTHYMIA: A condition characterized by recurring phases of elation and depression, its extreme form being Manic-Depressive Psychosis.

DEMENTIA: A condition of mental disintegration.

DETUMESCENCE: Subsidence from swelling. A term much used by Havelock Ellis to denote what he calls the second part of physiological sexual activity. The first part, tumescence or becoming tumid, is followed, with or without orgasm, by a comparatively rapid subsidence of the tumidity with decline in excitation.

DISFUNCTION: Disorder of function.

DISPLACEMENT: The transfer of an affect from the idea to which it was originally attached to an associated idea. It is one of the most important unconscious mechanisms in the production of phobias and other symptoms.

DRAMATIZATION: The representation of mental constellations in the form of drama, as in dreams, or in a real or active form.

EGO: That part of the id which has become modified by the impingement of external stimuli in such a way that it has become adapted to reality, reality testing and activity, and is credited with consciousness.

EGO-SYNTONIC: Fitting into the "harmony" of the ego and thus acceptable by it and helping to integrate it or build it up.

EROTIC: Sexual.

EROTOGENIC: Productive of erotic feelings.

EROTOGENIC ZONES: Sensitive areas of the body, stimulation of which gives rise to erotic feelings. These areas are often where mucous membranes join skin at the bodily orifices.

FAECAL: Of the nature of or containing bowel excrement.

FETISH: Anything which is attractive on account of its association, usually through unconscious elements, with erotic pleasure.

FIXATION: Arrest of a portion of the libidinal stream at an immature stage of development, either with reference to its erotogenic zone or with reference to its object-attachment or both. The level of a fixation determines the type of any psychosis or psycho-neurosis which later may occur, and the nature of its object attachment may determine its presenting form.

FRUSTRATION: The action of frustrating, or an obstacle or force which stands in the way of gratification or of the aim of an instinct.

GENITAL ORGANIZATION: That mature stage of libidinal development when the component instincts have become synthesized, with genital primacy and full capacity for object-love. In infancy it gives rise to the Oedipus complex and in later life to psycho-sexual union.

HETEROSEXUAL: Pertaining to Heterosexuality: Love for a person of the opposite sex, i.e. normal psycho-sexual development.

HOMOSEXUALITY: Sexual desire for a member of the same sex. (Cf. Inversion.)

ID : A concept of an undifferentiated primitive mind containing only innate urges, instincts, desires and wishes without consciousness or any appreciation of reality, and dominated entirely by the pleasure-principle.

IMAGO : The phantastic image formed in infancy from an erroneous conception of a loved or hated person.

INGEST : To take into the mouth or stomach.

INHIBITION : Restraint or frustration of an impulse by an opposing force, usually by an intra-psychic force. A frustration from within the psyche.

INSTINCTS : Innate patterns of discharge of tension.

INTRA-PSYCHIC : Within the mind.

INTROVERSION : The reversal of the libidinal stream from outward seeking to inward absorption, with consequent withdrawal of interest from the external world to the internal world of self. When extreme in degree it is one of the characteristics of schizophrenia, melancholia, hypochondriasis, etc.

INVERSION : (Sexual inversion). A condition of the sexual instinct being turned to persons in the image of oneself or of one's parent of the same sex as oneself; homosexuality. Havelock Ellis uses the term in a special sense to imply "*inborn* constitutional abnormality towards persons of the same sex. It is thus a narrower term than homosexuality, which includes all sexual attractions between persons of the same sex, even when seemingly due to the accidental absence of the natural objects of sexual attraction, a phenomenon of wide occurrence among all human races and among most of the higher animals." (Havelock Ellis, *Studies in the Psychology of Sex*, Vol. II, page 1.) "Inversion" is not generally used in this restricted sense, but more commonly as a synonym for homosexuality.

INVERTED-OEDIPUS : A reversal as regards sex of the Oedipus complex so that it is the parent of one's own sex instead of the opposite with whom one wishes to have intimacy.

LATENCY PERIOD : Period of life between the hypothetical end of infantile sexuality and the beginning of pubertal sexuality.

LIBIDINAL ORGANIZATION: The emotional pattern or system of sequences assumed by the libido. The libido passes through many stages in the course of development. From oral to genital the component instincts all have their own organization or pattern, but full maturity is reached only at the genital level of libidinal organization with its whole-object (persons-as-such) relationships.

LIBIDO: The energy of the sexual instinct and of its psycho-sexual component instincts. It is subject to many vicissitudes. For example, it can become aim-inhibited (i.e. orgasm-inhibited) and undergo unlimited displacement, even on to the person's own ego (narcissism, self-love) a-sexual objects and abstract ideas.

MANIC: Pertaining to mania, or the exalted phase of manic-depressive psychosis.

MASTURBATION: The act of producing sexual feeling by manual manipulation of the genital organ or other erotogenic zone.

NARCISSISM: Love of oneself.

NEUROLOGICAL: Pertaining to neurology: the science of organic disease of the brain and nervous system.

NEUROSIS: A functional nervous disease. By some writers, used to designate any illness of psychogenic origin.

NUCLEI: The centres or essences.

OBSESSIONAL NEUROSIS: A psychoneurosis characterized by the presence of obsessions which dominate the thought processes and behaviour of the patient. Compulsion neurosis.

OEDIPUS COMPLEX: As in the play *Oedipus Rex* by Sophocles, and as in the Greek legend on which it is founded, the unconscious of man from which these dramatizations originated, has been shown by psychoanalysis to contain a repressed constellation comprising a desire to displace the parent of the same sex and to possess sexually the parent of the opposite sex. It is something infinitely more powerful than commonsense that comes into effective conflict with the Oedipus constellation. It is specifically fear of castration which causes total repression of these desires and phantasies. Amongst the evidences of this repression there are the normal horror of incest, intimacy with the very person with whom one had since birth or before birth been most intimate, and the normal tendency to dramatize the repressed constellation in actuality, through the mechanism of displacement, by marrying a person in the image of the repressed imago, and for the persistence, at least in physical form, of a repugnance for those in the image of the once hated or displaced parent. Inability to deal adequately in these normal ways with the energy of the repressed complex and consequent regression to fixations at pre-Oedipus levels of libidinal organization, are the nuclear bases of psychoneurotic, characterological and mental disorders.

ONTOGENESIS: Development of the individual. (Cf. phylogenesis.)

OÖSPERM: A fertilized egg.

ORAL EROTISM: Erotic excitation from stimulation of the mouth or lips, the primary source of erotic feelings in babyhood and continuing in variable degree throughout life in spite of the acquisition of genital maturity with which it becomes associated as evidenced by the phenomenon of kissing and various habits and perversions.

ORGASM: The point at which erotic excitement reaches its acme and becomes involuntary. On the latter account it is suppressed by most persons in proportion to their prevailing anxiety and ill-health.

ORIFICE: An opening or aperture, usually where the mucous membrane, the lining of the body's internal channels, joins the skin or external covering.

PARAESTHESIA: Disordered sensation.

PARANOIA: A psychosis characterized by systematized delusions, commonly of persecution, love or hate. Freud considers that it has its source in repressed (unconscious) homosexual desires.

PARANOID: Pertaining to paranoia, or having some of the tendencies or characteristics of it. A lesser degree of paranoia.

PART-OBJECTS: Anatomical parts of a person which may be objects of intense love or hate without reference to the person as a whole. For instance, the baby loves the breast

R

or nipple (a part-object) without necessarily his mother as a "whole-object." The persistence of this tendency into adult life is a measure of various libidinal fixations.

PERVERSION: Any sexual act the object or mechanism of which is both biologically unsound and socially disapproved. Perversions are usually the manifestation of a psychosexual component instinct in substitution for mature genital sexuality.

PHALLIC: Pertaining to the Phallus, the erect penis or its image, worshipped in some religious systems as symbolizing generative power in nature.

PHYLOGENESIS: Biogenic development or evolution, e.g. of race or species. (Cf. Ontogenesis.)

PLEASURE-PRINCIPLE: A mental mechanism the object of which is solely to achieve pleasure by reduction of tension. It is a characteristic attribute of the id as manifested by its instinct drives. Contrast with "Reality Principle" a characteristic attribute of the ego.

PRAGMATIC: To do with practical or experimental observations and results.

PRE-GENITAL SEXUALITY: The infantile organization of the sexual pattern in which the component instincts and the pre-genital erotogenic zones such as oral, anal and phallic are absorbing the greater part of the libido.

PROGNOSTIC: Predictive. (Medicine): foretelling the course or results of an illness or condition.

PROJECTION: The attributing to persons or things outside oneself of mental processes, affects, etc., that originated within one's own mind and have been repressed from consciousness. It is a mechanism of release of the repressed with relief of tension, common in varying degrees to all minds with consequent impairment of their reality appreciation. It is very characteristic of paranoia.

PSYCHE: Mind.

PSYCHO-ANALYSIS: (i) A technical method introduced by Freud of bringing unconscious conflicts, complexes, etc., into consciousness by the process of Free Association of Thought, dream analysis and interpretation of the transference situation. (ii) The body of knowledge so obtained, including its theoretical formulations.

PSYCHOGENIC: Originating in the mind.

PSYCHONEUROTIC: Pertaining to psychoneurosis: psychogenic illness (i.e. without organic cause) characterized by derangement of the normal ways of gratification of the libido, due to unconscious conflict and, while leaving the ego or reason relatively unimpaired (cf. psychosis), giving rise to a variety of symptoms and pathological states which are capable of being relieved by psychotherapy. (Cf. Psychosis.)

PSYCHOPATHIC: Mentally abnormal.

PSYCHOPATHOLOGY: The study of morbidity in the psyche.

PSYCHO-SEXUAL: Relating to the psychic or emotional components of the sexual instinct.

PSYCHOSIS: Insanity. Mental illness which includes the ego or reason and therefore the person's relationship to reality. (Cf. Psychoneurosis.)

PSYCHOTHERAPY: The treatment of psychoneurotic, characterological and psychotic disorders by psychological methods, usually one of the forms of mind analysis, or by explanation, persuasion, re-education, relaxation, suggestion, hypnosis, vegetotherapy (Reich) or by occupational therapy.

PSYCHOTIC: Resembling a psychosis, or having some of the characteristics of psychosis.

PUNCHINELLO: A puppet.

RATIONALIZATION: The attributing of reasons for judgments, ideas or actions which are otherwise, usually emotionally, determined.

REACTION FORMATION: A character-trait, or its development, unconsciously designed to hold in check, conceal or contradict a tendency of an opposite kind. Thus obsessional cleanliness would be a reaction-formation against repressed dirtying tendencies. Disgust, shame and morality are other reaction formations.

REGRESSION: The reversal of the normal direction of the libidinal stream so that early infantile stages of its development (fixation points) are re-activated.

RE-ORIENTATE: Readjust; to alter one's ideas by a re-assessment of all the facts and principles and perhaps by the inclusion of new facts and considerations.

REPRESSION: The rejection from consciousness, by an unconscious mechanism, of mental material, concepts and affects which are unwelcome. Analysis has shown that this material remains active and dynamic in the unconscious, that the expenditure of repressing energy continues and the repressed commonly re-emerges in altered forms such as symptoms.

RESISTANCE: The mental force arrayed against the emergence into consciousness of painful, disagreeable or unwanted material, and which activates the mechanism of repression.

SCHIZOID: Having some of the characteristics of schizophrenia. Slightly schizophrenic.

SCHIZOPHRENIA: Split mind. A psychosis, usually in early life, characterized by repressed affect and interest with introversion and progressive dementia.

SOMATIC: Bodily, as distinct from mental. (In biology somatic would mean relating to the somotoplasm as distinct from germplasm.)

SUBLIMATION: The process of deflecting libido from sexual aims to interests of a non-sexual and socially approved nature.

SUPER-EGO: That part of the mental apparatus developed in early life by the mechanism of repressing frustrated impulses such as aggression, and projecting them on to the frustrators and subsequently introjecting them. Its function is largely to oppose the id, often unreasonably, and even to criticize and punish the ego if it tends to accept id demands. It is a sort of primitive unconscious conscience.

SURROGATE: The representation of a person in substitution for another and the assignation to him of the role properly or originally belonging to the other person.

TALION PUNISHMENT: Retaliatory punishment. Punishment equivalent to the crime. The principle of "eye for eye, tooth for tooth,"

TRANSFERENCE : A displacement of any affect from one person to another or from one idea to another. Specifically during analysis the affects originally felt during infancy for the parents become unconsciously displaced on to the person of the analyst so that the analysand feels towards him unjustifiable love and hate, etc., and has no insight into the phenomenon and its irrelevance. (See also pp. 226–7.)

TRAUMA : A morbid condition produced by an unpleasant experience.

TUMESCENCE : A swelling up. Specifically the turgidity produced in the sexual organs during the pre-orgasm stage of sexual excitement.

UNCONSCIOUS : A region of the psyche which contains mental processes and constellations which are ordinarily inaccessible to consciousness, commonly owing to the process of repression. The technique of mind analysis is especially designed to bring this unconscious material into consciousness by overcoming the resistances and repressing forces, as it is from the unconscious conflicts or complexes and their opposing forces or reaction formations that all symptoms emanate.

URETHRAL EROTISM : Erotic feelings produced by stimulation of the urethra (the urinary passage from the bladder to the exterior) during the passage of urine. It is one of the components of the genital sexual instinct.

WHOLE-OBJECT : The person as a whole, in contradistinction to exclusive interest in some anatomical part. (Cf. "part-objects.")

INDEX

ADJUSTMENT, 226
aetiology, 112, 142
affects, 110, 139
aggression, 109, 156
aggressive, 190, 246
allo erotic, 144, 249
ambivalence, 211
  unconscious, 86
ambivalent, 207
anaemia, 12
anal, 131, 150, 151, 152, 156, 157,
  159, 164, 240, 241, 242, 243
  activities, 150, 156
  experiences, 241
  level, 152, 241
  sphincter muscle, 155
analysis, 17, 18, 20, 24, 25, 59, 60,
  65, 69, 70, 75, 78, 83, 85, 89,
  91, 92, 95, 101, 105, 119, 123,
  124, 126, 132, 135, 136, 145,
  147, 148, 149, 150, 151, 153,
  158, 160, 162, 168, 169, 172,
  174, 175, 176, 177, 179, 182,
  183, 187, 189, 190, 191, 192,
  193, 196, 198, 199, 205, 206,
  207, 211, 214, 215, 218, 220,
  222, 223, 226, 227, 228, 229,
  230, 231, 232, 233, 236, 237,
  239, 242, 243, 246, 247, 249,
  250, 251
anger, 191
anus, 155
anxiety, 24, 26, 27, 29, 31, 33, 40,
  41, 43, 52, 53, 80, 84, 85, 86,
  87, 106, 120, 122, 123, 124, 125,
  126, 127, 128, 129, 130, 131,
  132, 133, 137, 150, 163, 188,
  199, 202, 245
  , acute, 27, 122, 132
  , sexual, 144
  state, 133
auto erotic, 144, 150, 152, 241, 247,
  248, 249
autonomic nervous system, 133

BABYHOOD, 46, 203, 229
Babyland, 60, 61
bacteriology, 12
beliefs, religious, 84, 85

CANNIBALISTIC PHANTASY, 240, 244,
  245
castrate, 84, 109, 132, 164

castrated, 122
castrating effects, 245
castration, 50, 96, 122, 123, 131,
  132, 133, 169, 245, 251
  anxiety, 123–5, 156, 159, 230
  elements, 134, 143
  phantasy, 131, 245
cataclysm, 181, 182
cataclysmic, 234
censorship, 75, 181
character, 55, 226, 240
  formation, 239, 240
  traits, 126, 144, 244
characterological basis, 17
  structure, 20
characterology, 145
child-father pattern, 197
child-parent situation, 147
childhood, 46, 49, 59, 60, 67, 193,
  209, 220, 226
  pattern, 55
climax, 188, 190, 232, 245
compensation, 80
compensatory mechanism, 250
compulsion, 38, 226, 234, 249, 251
conflict, 21, 22, 23, 31, 32, 34, 38,
  46, 106, 118, 134, 135, 143, 161,
  169, 222, 223, 225, 249
  , repressed, 24
  , sexual, 11, 51
conscious, 62, 89, 101, 105, 125, 138,
  139, 154, 170, 200, 213, 214,
  250
  level, 105, 126, 166, 232
  mind, 51, 95
  plane, 52, 60, 84, 93, 101
consciousness, 36, 74, 75, 77, 89,
  109, 125, 132, 135, 147, 167,
  172, 190, 206, 247, 249
control, 67, 70, 141, 191, 234
conversion hysteria, 134, 135, 138
  symptoms, 142
crisis, 190
cult, 158, 159
cultural, 240, 249
culture, 112, 158, 163, 250

DEFENCE, 24, 92, 123, 193, 225
  resistance, 24, 139
delusions, 19, 83, 159, 160
depressed, 67, 92, 189
depression, 18, 65, 92, 93, 179, 180,
  191, 195, 196, 197, 203, 251
depressive, 18

GEORGE ALLEN & UNWIN LTD
LONDON: 40 MUSEUM STREET, W.C.1
CAPE TOWN: 58–60 LONG STREET
TORONTO: 91 WELLINGTON STREET WEST
BOMBAY: 15 GRAHAM ROAD, BALLARD ESTATE
CALCUTTA: 17 CENTRAL AVENUE, P.O. DHARAMTALA,
WELLINGTON, N.Z.: 8 KINGS CRESCENT, LOWER HUTT
SYDNEY, N.S.W.: BRADBURY HOUSE, 55 YORK STREET

Psychoanalysis Today

by Ernest Jones, A. A. Brill, Edward Glover, Fritz Wittels, Melanie Klein and others.   *Demy 8vo.   25s.*

" This important book contains information of the greatest value . . . No better exposition of the Freudian doctrines could have been given to the class of reader for whom it is evidentally intended, the intelligent layman."—KENNETH WALKER in *The Sunday Times.*

Nervous Disorders and Character

by J. G. McKenzie.   *Cr. 8vo.   5s.*

" Professor McKenzie is to be heartily congratulated on a book which deserves, and is sure to obtain, a very wide public."— *Christian World.*

What is Psychoanalysis ?

by Ernest Jones, M.D.   *Cr. 8vo.   7s. 6d.*

What is Psychoanalysis ? is a brief account of the basic facts of a new and growing science.   It begins with a definition of the word psychoanalysis and gives a brief history of the subject.   Part two examines specific aspects such as The Unconscious, Sexuality and Dreams.   Part three discusses the applications of psychoanalysis to everyday subjects—Medicine, Sociology, Politics, Literature and Religion.

First published in America some years ago, the book required little change to bring it into line with today's views.   It is written with a minimum of technical terms, and includes an up-to-date bibliography.   The general reader will find a firm foundation upon which to build a clear understanding of psychoanalysis.

Emotional Problems of Living

by O. Spurgeon English, M.D., and Gerald H. J. Pearson, M.D.   *Demy 8vo.   16s.*

Emotional Problems of Living describes the different frictions generated within the individual or through his contacts with his environment.   Its purpose is to give a point of view and a therapeutic approach which will reduce to a minimum those conflicts that tend towards the neurotic pattern.   The book takes full cognizance of psychoanalytic thought, since the authors feel that Freudian psychoanalysis is the best approach to the understanding of personality.   From birth to old age, the continuing development of the personality is discussed, and the reader is made familiar with the commoner deviations from the normal that occur at each particular period of life.   In conclusion, a brief presentation of methods of treatment is offered.

The Inner Experience of a Psychoanalyst
by Theodor Reik. *Demy 8vo.*

"The following pages," says the author in his Introduction, "tell the story of the strange adventure which is the most important work of a psychoanalyst : the story of an expedition into the last dark continent on earth." His book, which is unique in psychoanalytical literature is in fact an attempt to analyse the analyst at work, to show the processes of his mind and how he arrives at insight into the emotional recesses of his patient's mind, either as a result of long and patient mining or of sudden flashes emerging from unconscious depths. Dr. Reik subjects himself to searching analyses, showing how his own dreams and inner thoughts help him to understand his patient's unconscious conflicts.

The author is an early pupil of Freud, and has been in practice as an analyst for thirty-seven years. His book is documented by a great number of cases, selected for their interest and revealed with deep understanding. They show that psychoanalysis is a two-way process, an inter-play of the doctor's and the patient's unconscious, and that the doctor has to learn something of himself before he can help the man on the couch.

This difficult subject is handled in a manner that makes it understandable to any layman, and it is fascinating to read.

Psychology and Mental Health
by J. A. Hadfield, Lecturer in Psychopathology and Mental Hygiene, London University. *Demy 8vo. 18s.*

This book describes the origin and behaviour disorders and the psychoneuroses especially as regards their causes in early childhood. Most psychologists now agree that such disorders as hysteria, sex perversion, the obsessions and anxiety states, as well as many behaviour disorders and delinquencies, find their roots in childhood experiences. If this is the case it should be possible, by dealing directly with such early aberrations to prevent them from developing into full-blown neurotic disorders which may take years to cure.

The purpose of this book is to describe the early causes of these disorders with a view to their treatment, but more particularly to their prevention. It embodies the result of over thirty years experience in the treatment of patients suffering from these disorders, and the views here maintained are fully illustrated from clinical examples throughout.

Guiding the Child

by Alfred Adler and associates. *Cr. 8vo. 8s. 6d.*

This book, now in its third impression, was the result of experience gained by a group of physicians and teachers who, during the 1920's, organised a number of child guidance clinics in different parts of Europe under the leadership of Alfred Adler. It makes a closely knit account of inestimable value to the welfare worker, the physician and the forward-looking parent.

The Education of Children

by Alfred Adler. *Cr. 8vo. 3rd Impression. 8s. 6d.*

" Throughout it is informed by a profound knowledge of human nature . . . no parent can read Dr. Adler's book without feeling happier about his task . . . the general outlook is invigorating and instructive to a high degree."—*Times Literary Supplement.*

Clinical Psychology

by Charles Berg, M.D., D.P.M., *Author of " Deep Analysis "*
Demy 8vo. 25s.

Dr. Berg. has an extraordinary flair for presenting a difficult subject in a most realistic and attractive manner, without sacrifice of scientific essentials.

The patients are made to speak for themselves, with the result that we feel actually present at the analytical sessions, sharing the most intimate details of each individual's life and feelings. Throughout it is alive with real, vivid clinical material. The reader is led through a panorama of troubled minds and disturbed emotions—from the simplest worries and anxieties, through increasing severity of stresses, to incipient major disorders.

The whole subject of treatment is reviewed and expounded in compendious detail, concluding with a critical review and revolutionary suggestions for the future.

" Here is something as different as possible from the usual medical text-book. Illustrative cases of various types are described, and in the ' samples,' so to speak, taken from the sessions, one hears the authentic voice of the emotionally-racked patient. Factual information there is in abundance, and the author's description and classification of the types of nervous and mental disorders is of the greatest value."—*The Psychologist.*

The Road to Love

AVOIDING THE NEUROTIC PATTERN.

by Gwilym O. Roberts, Consulting Psychologist and Advanced Research Worker in the Department of Psychiatry, Leeds Medical School.

With a Foreword by Dr. David R. Mace and a note by Professor William Brown. *Cr. 8vo. 9s. 6d.*

Much has been written on love and marriage by writers who have had little if any scientific and advanced research grounding in this field. The author of this refreshing book on preparing for successful marriage is a consulting psychologist and an authority on the application of rigorously scientific techniques to marriage guidance. It is an absorbing summary of the research findings of biologists, psychologists, sociologists and psychiatrists, and is written in simple, practical terms with a frankness and popular flair that holds the reader from the very beginning.

The book is divided into three parts dealing with the growth of the love life, fixations, regressions and retardations of growth ; and mature love. The treatment ranges from the " infancy stage " right through to the " monogamous stage " and provides psychological guide-posts for young people, parents, teachers and social workers.

Guide to Marriage

by Leslie Tizard. *Cr. 8vo. Third Impression. 7s. 6d.*

" Full of practical and psychological wisdom . . . it handles with the most complete frankness the physical side of marriage."

" The book is intended for engaged couples, yet not only they, but many who have been married for some years, will be grateful for it. It has a lively style, and is easy to follow."—*Record.*

" Gives the facts with lucid frankness, but in a Christian setting and with friendly good humour . . . I wish this *Guide* could be available to every couple who apply to be married in Church, and I confidently commend it to ministers and leaders of youth."—*Congregational Quarterly.*

" An honest book . . . not only would it be of use to those about to be married, but to many who are already married. It is written simply and with a matter-of-fact directness that highly commends it."—*Inquirer.*

All prices are net.

GEORGE ALLEN & UNWIN, LTD.